Sing for Joy

A SONGBOOK FOR YOUNG CHILDREN

Compiled and Edited by

NORMAN *and* MARGARET MEALY

Illustrated by KARLA KUSKIN

THE SEABURY PRESS · GREENWICH, CONNECTICUT

Sing for Joy was prepared under the direction of the Department of Christian Education of the National Council of the Protestant Episcopal Church in the United States of America as a part of THE SEABURY SERIES.

THE REV. NORMAN MEALY is Assistant Professor of Church Music at the Church Divinity School of the Pacific, Berkeley, California. His wife, MARGARET, was formerly Assistant Professor of Music at Skidmore College, Saratoga Springs, New York, and Lecturer in Christian Education at St. Margaret's House, Berkeley, California.

LIBRARY OF CONGRESS CATALOGUE CARD NUMBER: M 61-1003

© THE SEABURY PRESS, INCORPORATED, 1961

MUSIC AUTOGRAPHY BY *Maxwell Weaner*.   DESIGN BY *Andor Braun*.

PRINTED IN THE UNITED STATES OF AMERICA

Preface

"O come let us sing unto the Lord." This is a call that rings throughout the Bible. Down through the years, the people of God have raised their voices to Him in songs of prayer and praise and thanksgiving.

The songs in this book are about God and His world and have been compiled especially for young children aged three to eight. There are songs to sing at home, at church, and at church school, so that children, too, may "make a joyful noise unto the Lord." Some of the songs are for serious and thoughtful moments; others for fun and activity.

There are songs short and simple enough for preschoolers to sing by themselves, and longer ones for parents and teachers to sing to them. For older children in the first, second, and third grades, there are songs to sing all through the day, wherever they are, whatever they are doing.

There is no need for a parent or teacher to be a skilled singer or pianist to use this book. With a few exceptions, the music has been kept simple. Anyone with a year or two of piano training will be able to play the two- and three-part harmonizations, and nearly all the songs may be sung without any accompaniment at all.

The age-level at which the songs will generally be most useful has been marked beside each title: "N" (nursery) indicates songs suitable for three- and four-year-olds; "K" (kindergarten), those for five-year-olds; and "P" (primary), the songs for children in first, second, and third grades. However, many of the songs marked "P" may be used with kindergartners, and many "K" songs may be sung with nursery children.

FROM THE HYMNAL 1940...

THIS book grew primarily from the need to *supplement,* for young children, the Episcopal *Hymnal 1940.* It is not intended to be a substitute for it. Children should know the great hymns of our Christian heritage, especially those sung in their parish. Yet many hymns have little or no meaning for them because of difficult imagery and old-fashioned language. We have, therefore, chosen many good melodies from the Hymnal and given them new words. In most cases, these melodies already appear in the Hymnal with more than one set of words. This practice is nothing new—the psalm-singing congregations of early America used a small set of melodies to sing their way through the whole psalter!

Except for a few short phrases and refrains for very young children, we have not included any texts from *The Hymnal 1940.* Instead, we have provided a list of selections from the Hymnal which clergymen and teachers have found useful for their children. You will find the list at the end of this book (pages 131–135). It is grouped under helpful topics such as Christmas, Praise, God the Creator, and so forth. References to this list are included after each section of songs to help parents and teachers use both books more creatively with children.

FROM OTHER SOURCES...

THE words and music in this book have been gathered from many different sources. We have drawn from the hymnals of other churches in this country and abroad, from the suggestions of writers and teachers across the land, and from the work of contemporary poets. Many people wrote new poems and musical settings for the collection.

Many traditional folk-melodies have found their way into these pages, and from the early hymnbooks of New England and the Southern Atlantic states we have chosen melodies that are beautiful, expressive, and easy to sing. Several are modal in character, unlike the familiar major and minor scale patterns. Since their original texts were often bright and vigorous, these colorful melodies should not be sung as if they were "sad."

A children's songbook, published today, should reflect the musical sounds of today's composers, and we have therefore included several new works by contemporary composers. At first, these songs may seem difficult to sing and to play, but don't avoid them because they are a little "different." Children soon find them as easy as other songs, and delight in the new sounds—as they frequently do with the music of Bartok and Stravinsky.

IN CONCLUSION...

SINGING is a common experience, which, like bicycle-riding, needs practice and encouragement. Some children are better at it than others. Singing skills, like speaking skills, grow gradually. Youngsters who grow up in singing families will enthusiastically join their voices to the praise of God in our singing church. So, let everyone in the family of God sing for joy of Him who visited and redeemed His people.

Norman and Margaret Mealy

Acknowledgments

WITHOUT the encouragement and help of a number of people this book would not have been. A Children's Music Book Committee at the Department of Christian Education of the National Council of the Protestant Episcopal Church has given us invaluable suggestions for content and organization. That committee included its chairman, Mrs. John Harrell, Preschool Editor; the Rev. David Hunter, Director of the Department; the Rev. William Sydnor, Executive Secretary of the Curriculum Development Division; the Rev. Edric Weld, Associate Secretary of the same Division; Miss Agnes Hickson, Primary Editor; Miss Elinor M. Eccles of the Children's Division; the Rev. William Schmidgall, member of the Joint Commission on Church Music; the Rev. John Harrell, Executive Secretary of the Division of Audio-Visual Education; Miss Casey G. Miller, representative of The Seabury Press; and the committee's secretary, Mrs. Philip Leighton, and, later, Miss Sue Ondayko.

Special thanks are due also to the composers and poets who have gladly contributed their talents to the children who will be singing from this book.

Clergy and teachers have offered many suggestions about useful materials. To them and to those children in church schools scattered throughout the country who tested many of these songs in their classrooms, we express our appreciation. Readers of our preliminary manuscript have also given us much helpful guidance. We are indebted to Dr. Paul Schwartz, Professor of Church Music at Bexley Hall, Gambier, Ohio, for reading the proofs.

We are grateful to librarians who have made their professional knowledge (and their books) available to us. We especially remember the kindness of those in the children's room of the Boston Public Library, and those in charge of the splendid hymnal collection at the Union Theological Seminary in New York, the library at Tucker House in Greenwich, the children's music collection at St. Margaret's House in Berkeley, and the Arthur M. Farlander Music Collection at the Church Divinity School of the Pacific in Berkeley.

For permissions granted and for assistance in tracking down copyright owners we thank the many publishers who have been generous in their cooperation.

Finally, we thank our own two song testers, David and Mark, for helping their parents discover the joy that music brings to preschoolers.

All harmonizations have been especially prepared for this book by the editors with the exception of the following numbers: 1, 4, 11, 15–18, 23, 28, 29, 32, 45, 47, 53–56, 59, 61, 64, 79, 90, 94, 97, 101–103, 109, 114, 116, 123, 125, 126, 138, 139, 144–146, 149, 154, 155.

We have made every effort to discover the owners of copyrights and to secure permission for the use of their verses and melodies. If there is any copyright infringement or error in acknowledgment, it is unintentional. We hope the owners will notify us of any such errors and will pardon them.

N. M.
M. M.

Contents

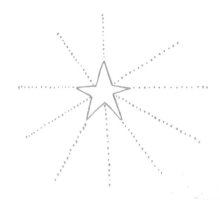

O sing to the Lord a new song;
   sing to the Lord, all the earth!
Sing to the Lord, bless his name;
   tell of his salvation from day to day.
Declare his glory among the nations,
   his marvelous works among all the peoples!

. . . .

Let the heavens be glad, and let the earth rejoice;
   let the sea roar, and all that fills it;
   let the field exult, and everything in it!
Then shall all the trees of the wood sing for joy
   before the Lord. . .

PSALM 96

God in Christ came into our world to
all people, young or old, great or small,
and He is with us always. O come let us adore
Him with thanksgiving and joy.

He Hath Visited

and Redeemed His People

THE CHRISTIAN YEAR

THE CHURCH

1

P

The Annunciation

F. ABAIR

Plainsong

Lightly and easily.

1. One day while Ma - ry knelt in prayer She saw an an - gel stand - ing there.
2. Now Ma - ry feared and bowed her head. "Oh, do not fear," the an - gel said,
3. Then Ma - ry spoke the bless - ed word: "Be - hold the Hand-maid of the Lord.

His glo - ry filled the dwell - ing place. He said to her, "Hail, full of Grace!"
"For God shall send His Son to thee. His ho - ly Mo - ther, thou shalt be."
As thou hast said, so be it done." The Son of God be - came her Son.

Words reprinted by permission of the copyright owners, Gregorian Institute of America.
Harmonization by Winfred Douglas; reprinted by permission of The Church Pension Fund.

This melody, "Conditor alme," appears in *The Hymnal 1940* at #6 and elsewhere in this book at #4 and #15. See page 131 for suggestions about singing
and accompanying plainsong.

The Little King of the World Came Down

NANCY BYRD TURNER, alt.

NORMAN AND MARGARET MEALY

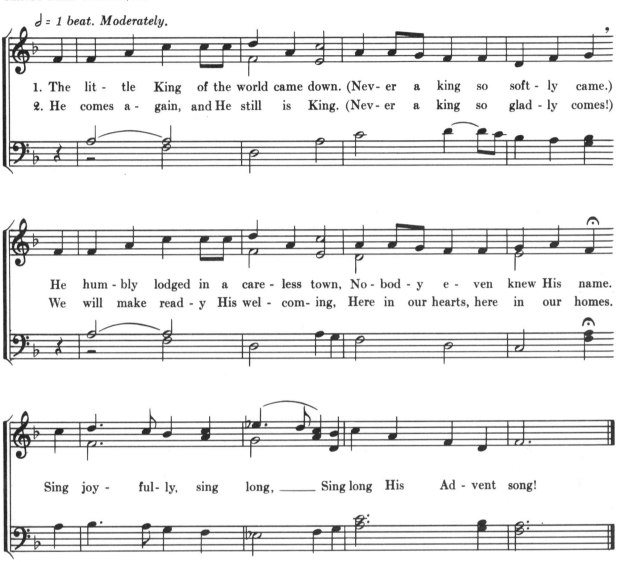

♩ = 1 beat. *Moderately.*

1. The lit - tle King of the world came down. (Nev - er a king so soft - ly came.)
2. He comes a - gain, and He still is King. (Nev - er a king so glad - ly comes!)

He hum - bly lodged in a care - less town, No - bod - y e - ven knew His name.
We will make read - y His wel - com - ing, Here in our hearts, here in our homes.

Sing joy - ful - ly, sing long, ____ Sing long His Ad - vent song!

Words from *Hymns for Primary Worship*. Copyright, 1946, by The Westminster Press. Used by permission.

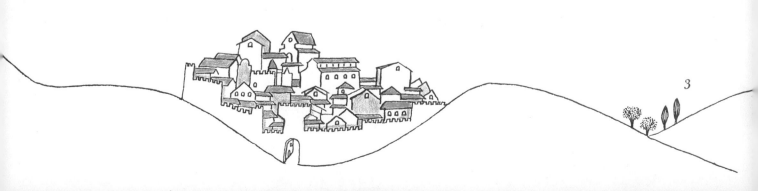

3

Jesus Is Coming

PHYLLIS SAUNDERS, alt.

Welsh Carol

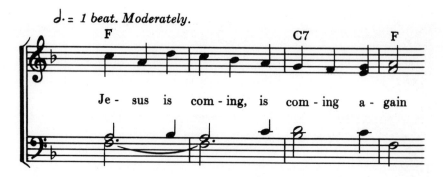

Je - sus is com - ing, is com - ing a - gain

And _ bring - ing His mes - sage of Good - will to men.

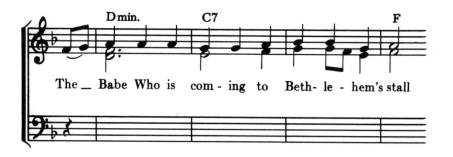

The _ Babe Who is com - ing to Beth - le - hem's stall

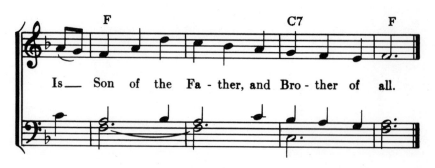

Is _ Son of the Fa - ther, and Bro - ther of all.

Words reprinted by permission of the National Society, London, England. This is the second
stanza of the song "Christmas Is Coming."

The Trip to Bethlehem

F. ABAIR

Plainsong

Lightly and easily.

1. St. Jo - seph brushed the don - key neat, Put Ma - ry in the sad - dle seat,
2. They trav - eled on for ma - ny days A - long the wind - ing dust - y ways.

Then took his staff of hick - ory limb, And start - ed off for Beth - le - hem.
But no com - plaint was heard from them, A - trav - 'ling down to Beth - le - hem.

Words reprinted by permission of the copyright owners, Gregorian Institute of America.
Harmonization by Winfred Douglas; reprinted by permission of The Church Pension Fund.

This melody, "Conditor alme," appears in *The Hymnal 1940* at #6 and elsewhere in this book at #1 and #15. See page 131 for suggestions about singing
and accompanying plainsong.

For a list of appropriate Advent hymns in *The Hymnal 1940,* see page 132.

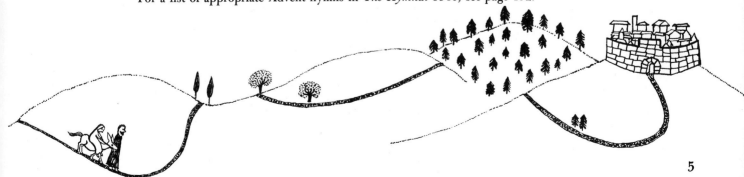

The Birthday of the Lord

MARY JANE CARR

Southern Harmony

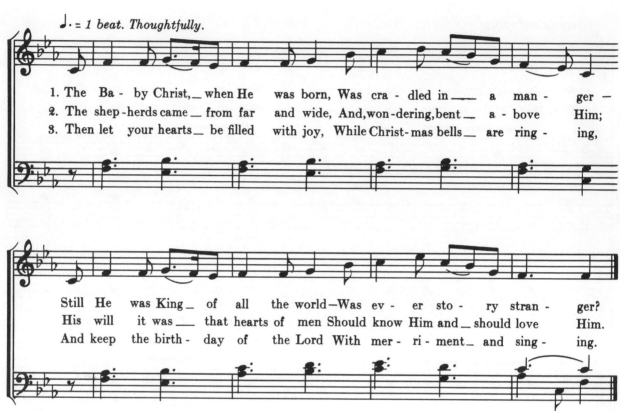

♩. = 1 beat. Thoughtfully.

1. The Ba - by Christ,__ when He was born, Was cra - dled in __ a man - ger —
2. The shep - herds came __ from far and wide, And, won - der - ing, bent __ a - bove Him;
3. Then let your hearts __ be filled with joy, While Christ - mas bells __ are ring - ing,

Still He was King __ of all the world—Was ev - er sto - ry stran - ger?
His will it was __ that hearts of men Should know Him and __ should love Him.
And keep the birth - day of the Lord With mer - ri - ment __ and sing - ing.

Words copyright © 1941 by Mary Jane Carr. Reprinted by permission of McIntosh and Otis, Inc.

Baby Jesus

ELIZABETH McE. SHIELDS, alt.

W. LAWRENCE CURRY

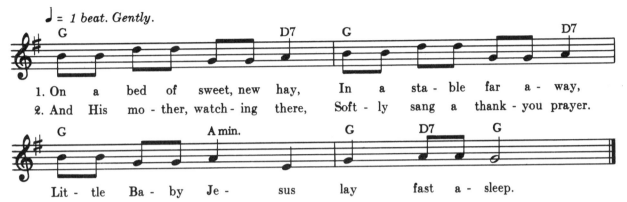

♩ = 1 beat. Gently.

1. On a bed of sweet, new hay, In a sta - ble far a - way,
2. And His mo - ther, watch - ing there, Soft - ly sang a thank - you prayer.

Lit - tle Ba - by Je - sus lay fast a - sleep.

Melody from *When the Little Child Wants to Sing*. Copyright, 1935, by the Presbyterian Board of Christian Education. Used by permission.

See Jesus Our Saviour

Traditional American, alt.

Traditional American

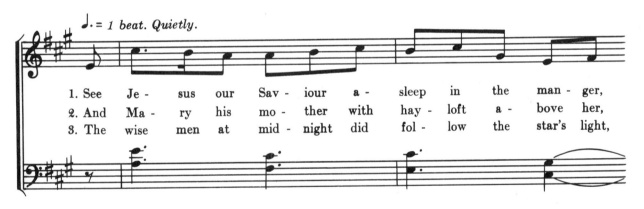

♩. = 1 beat. Quietly.

1. See Je - sus our Sav - iour a - sleep in the man - ger,
2. And Ma - ry his mo - ther with hay - loft a - bove her,
3. The wise men at mid - night did fol - low the star's light,

Ah -

Words and melody from *Ballads, Carols, and Tragic Legends from the Southern Appalachian Mountains*, collected and arranged by John Jacob Niles. Copyright 1937 by G. Schirmer, Inc.; reprinted by permission.

Children can sing the "Ah" refrain before they learn the verses.

Mary Had a Baby

Stanza 1: Traditional American
Stanzas 2 and 3: RUTH CRAWFORD SEEGER

Traditional American

♩ = 1 beat. Brightly.

1. Ma - ry had a Ba - by, Aye, Lord,
2. Shep - herds came to see Him, Aye, Lord,
3. Wise men brought Him pres - ents, Aye, Lord,

Ma - ry had a Ba - by, Aye, my Lord,
Shep - herds came to see Him, Aye, my Lord,
Wise men brought Him pres - ents, Aye, my Lord,

Ma - ry had a Ba - by, Aye, Lord,
Shep - herds came to see Him, Aye, Lord, Ba - by
Wise men brought Him pres - ents, Aye, Lord,

Je - sus in a man - ger at Beth - le - hem.

The word *aye,* pronounced "eye," means "yes." Children will soon learn to sing back the phrases "Aye, Lord" and "Aye, my Lord." Later, divide the group so that some sing these phrases and others the verses. Or one child may sing the verses, everyone else the answering phrases. Encourage the children to make up additional verses.

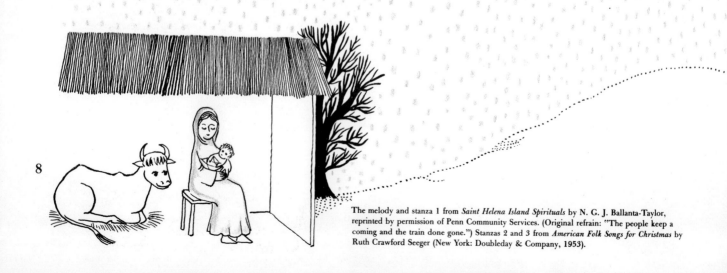

8

The melody and stanza 1 from *Saint Helena Island Spirituals* by N. G. J. Ballanta-Taylor, reprinted by permission of Penn Community Services. (Original refrain: "The people keep a coming and the train done gone.") Stanzas 2 and 3 from *American Folk Songs for Christmas* by Ruth Crawford Seeger (New York: Doubleday & Company, 1953).

Christmas Is Remembering

ELSIE BINNS

NORMAN AND MARGARET MEALY

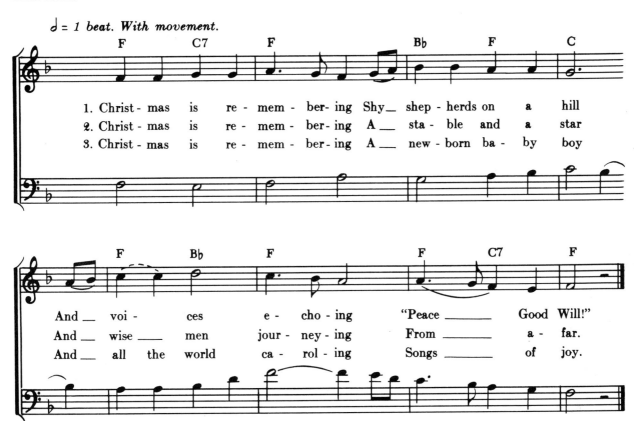

♩ = 1 beat. With movement.

| F | C7 | F | Bb | F | C |

1. Christ - mas is re - mem - ber - ing Shy __ shep - herds on a hill
2. Christ - mas is re - mem - ber - ing A __ sta - ble and a star
3. Christ - mas is re - mem - ber - ing A __ new - born ba - by boy

| F | Bb | F | F | C7 | F |

And __ voi - ces e - cho - ing "Peace _____ Good Will!"
And __ wise __ men jour - ney - ing From _____ a - far.
And __ all the world ca - rol - ing Songs _____ of joy.

10

As We Deck Our Houses

CHRISTINE FLEMING HEFFNER   Based on a melody by W. A. MOZART

1. As we deck our hou - ses With twin- kling lights __ a - flame, __
2. As we hear the car - ols __ All a - bout __ the town, __
3. As we give our pres - ents __ To the ones __ we love, __

So the stars shone o - ver- head The night that Ba - by came. __
Shep- herds heard the an - gels sing The night the Lord __ came down. __
So God gave the great - est Gift: His true Son from __ a - bove. __

Words © Christine Fleming Heffner 1961. From a longer poem, "The Candle in the Window."

This song is fun for families or classes to sing while decorating a tree or wrap-
ping presents.

11

Now Every Child

ELEANOR FARJEON   LEO SOWERBY

Now ev - ery Child that dwells on earth, Stand up, stand up and sing!

The pass - ing night has giv - en birth Un - to the Chil - dren's King.

Sing sweet as the flute, Sing clear as the horn,

retarding

Sing joy of the Chil - dren Come Christ - mas the morn!

More slowly

Lit - tle Christ Je - sus Our Bro - ther is born.

The words (the first stanza of a longer poem) are from *Come Christmas* by Eleanor Farjeon.
Reprinted by permission of the author, J. B. Lippincott Company, and A. Watkins.

A group of boys and girls could learn this song as a special contribution to a Christmas service.

11

Christ Was Born in Bethlehem

Traditional American, alt.   Traditional American

Melody from *American Folk Songs for Children* by Ruth Crawford Seeger, published by
Doubleday & Company; reprinted by permission of Charles Seeger.

This melody appears also at #39 with words appropriate for **Easter** or any Sunday.

The Friendly Beasts

Twelfth-Century Carol, alt.   Traditional French

♩. = 1 beat. Moderately.

1. Je - sus our bro - ther, strong ~~Kind~~ and good,
2. "I," said the don - key, shag - gy and brown,
3. "I," said the cow, all white __ and red,

Was hum - bly born __ in a sta - ble rude,
"I car - ried His mo-ther up - hill and down,
"I gave Him my man - ger __ for His bed,

And the friend - ly beasts __ a - round Him stood,
I __ car - ried His mo-ther to Beth - le - hem town;
I __ gave Him my hay __ to pil - low His head,

Je - sus our bro - ther, strong ~~Kind~~ and good.
I," said the don - key shag - gy and brown.
I," said the cow all white __ and red.

4.

"I," said the sheep with
   curly horn,
"I gave Him my wool for
   His blanket warm,
He wore my coat on
   Christmas morn;
I," said the sheep with
   curly horn.

5.

"I," said the dove, from the
   rafters high,
"I cooed Him to sleep that
   He should not cry,
We cooed Him to sleep,
   my mate and I;
I," said the dove, from the
   rafters high.

6.

Thus every beast by some
   good spell,
In the stable dark was glad
   to tell,
Of the gift he gave
   Emmanuel,
The gift he gave Emmanuel.

Words (alt.) from *Welcome Christmas*, edited by Anne Thaxter Eaton; reprinted by permission of The Viking Press.

14

Bethl'em Lay A-Sleeping

FRANCES B. WOOD, alt.   Polish carol

♩ = 1 beat. Not fast.

1. Beth - l'em lay a - sleep - ing, Long, long a - go;
2. Kings came to a - dore Him, Long, long a - go;
3. An - gels sweet - ly sing - ing, Long, long a - go;

Twin - kling stars were peep - ing, Long, long a - go.
They knelt down be - fore Him, Long, long a - go.
Sent His prais - es ring - ing, Long, long a - go.

When to earth a Ba - by came, The lit - tle Je - sus was His name, Long, long a - go.
Wan-d'ring shep-herds left their sheep To see their lit - tle Lord a - sleep, Long, long a - go.
Chil - dren, too, their love may bring To Him who came to be our King, Long, long a - go.

Words reprinted by permission of Concordia Publishing House, St. Louis, Mo.

Children can sing "Long, long ago" before they learn the rest of the song.

For other Christmas songs, see:

4	The Trip to Bethlehem	K P
23	Because We Cannot Reach to God	P
37	Happy Easter [Christmas] Morning (see note)	N K
57	The Sunday [Christmas] Bells Are Ringing (see note)	N K
67	The Lord Has Done Great Things (see note)	K P
151	We're Making Valentines [Christmas cards] (see note)	N K

For a list of appropriate Christmas hymns in *The Hymnal 1940,* see page 132.

The Wise Men

F. ABAIR

Lightly and easily.

Now there ap- peared a   bril - liant Star Which led the Wise Men from a- far.

They came and, kneel- ing down, a - dored And of - fered gifts to Christ, the Lord.

Words reprinted by permission of the copyright owners, Gregorian Institute of America.
Harmonization by Winfred Douglas; reprinted by permission of The Church Pension Fund.

This melody, "Conditor alme," appears in *The Hymnal 1940* at #6 and elsewhere in this book at #1 and #4. See page 131 for suggestions about singing and accompanying plainsong.

The Three Kings

LILLIAN HICKS BALLARD   LILLIAN HICKS BALLARD

We have come from far a - way To see the Christ - child on the hay.

Kings are we and gifts we bring To lay be - fore our Heav'n - ly King.

Al - le - lu - ia! Al - le - lu - ia! Al - le - lu - ia!

Over the Hills

PHYLLIS SAUNDERS, alt.

PHYLLIS SAUNDERS

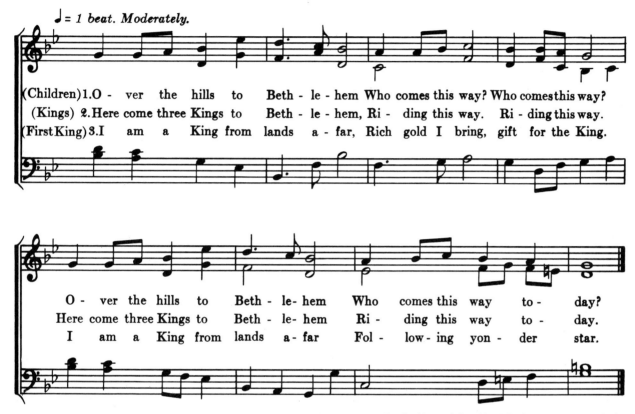

♩ = 1 beat. Moderately.

(Children) 1. O - ver the hills to Beth - le - hem Who comes this way? Who comes this way?
(Kings) 2. Here come three Kings to Beth - le - hem, Ri - ding this way. Ri - ding this way.
(First King) 3. I am a King from lands a - far, Rich gold I bring, gift for the King.

O - ver the hills to Beth - le-hem Who comes this way to - day?
Here come three Kings to Beth - le-hem Ri - ding this way to - day.
I am a King from lands a - far Fol - low-ing yon - der star.

Reprinted by permission of the National Society, London, England.

(Second King) 4. I am a King from lands afar
Incense I bring, gift for the King.
I am a King from lands afar
Following yonder star.

(Third King) 5. I am a King from lands afar
And Myrrh I bring, gift for the King.
I am a King from lands afar
Following yonder star.

(Children) 6. Over the hills from Bethlehem
Who rides away? Who rides away?
Over the hills from Bethlehem
Who rides another way?

(Kings) 7. Three Kings have gone from Bethlehem
Riding away. Riding away.
Three Kings have gone from Bethlehem
Home by another way.

From East to West

18
P

SEDULIUS
Tr. JOHN ELLERTON

VERNON DE TAR

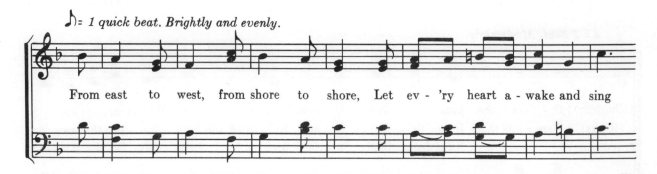

From east to west, from shore to shore, Let ev-'ry heart a-wake and sing

The Ho-ly Child Whom Ma-ry bore, The Christ, the ev-er-last-ing King.

Words: "A solis ortus cardine" by Sedulius (d. c. 450), tr. John Ellerton (d. 1893) and
compilers of *Hymns Ancient and Modern*.

Good News

19
K P

Evangelist ABRAHAM MUMOL, alt.

Native Buzi (Liberian) tune, alt.
From the Rev. GEORGE R. FLORA

1. I have heard good news to-day!
2. Je-sus is the Son of God! Who has told ___ you?
3. Je-sus is the friend of all!

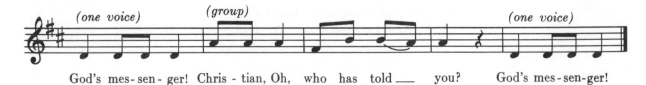

God's mes-sen-ger! Chris-tian, Oh, who has told ___ you? God's mes-sen-ger!

From *The Whole World Singing*, compiled by Edith Lovell Thomas. Used by permission of
United Lutheran Church Women and Friendship Press, Inc.

Children may enjoy accompanying this song with drums and rattles, as the Liberian
tribesmen sometimes do.

Far Away in Old Judea

WALTER J. MATHAMS, alt.

Plymouth Collection

♩ = 1 beat. *In a flowing style.*

1. Far a - way in old Ju - de - a Lived the gen - tle Lord of Love.
2. Oh, what won-drous tales he told them Of our Fa- ther's thought-ful care;

Hap - py chil - dren gath - ered round him Ev - ery - where that he might move,
How he loves us, leads us, keeps us, Ev - ery day and ev - ery - where;

And they some-times left their play, — Just to fol - low him all day.
That we ne - ver need to fear, — Since his help is al - ways near!

Words from *Song and Play for Children*, by Danielson and Conant. Copyright, The Pilgrim Press. Used by permission.

This melody, "Pleading Saviour," appears in *The Hymnal 1940* at #117 and #511.

19

21
KP

In Galilee Beside the Sea

ALICE M. PULLEN

HAL SAUNDERS, Jnr.

♩ = 1 beat. Moderately.

1. In Gal - i - lee be - side the sea Lit - tle girls and boys
2. In Gal - i - lee be - side the sea Peo - ple who were sad

Came to Je - sus, talked with Je - sus; Je - sus shared their joys.
Came to Je - sus, sent for Je - sus; Je - sus made them glad.

For other Epiphany songs, see:

45 May the Gospel of the Lord P
53 Brave Men P
54 The Church the Family of God P
111 God's Children Speak in Different Tongues P
112 It Makes No Difference, East or West P
120 For All God's Children KP

For a list of appropriate Epiphany hymns in *The Hymnal 1940*, see page 132.

Here Are My Hands

RUTH B. PIERCE

Traditional **German**

1. Here are my hands to work for Thee. Take them and make them work — for Thee.
2. Here are my eyes to see the right. Take them and make them see — the right.

Here are my feet to walk Thy way. Take them and make them walk — Thy way.
Here is my life to give to Thee. Take me and make me more — like Thee. A - men.

This melody, "Mendon," appears in *The Hymnal 1940* at #218, #291, and #378.

Because We Cannot Reach to God

CAROL CHRISTOPHER DRAKE

WILLIAM B. SCHMIDGALL

Be - cause we can - not reach to God, God reached to us,

and came as Je - sus, not that He might know our lives, but we know Him.

24
P

Dear Lord Jesus

ANDREW LEE

Traditional Irish

𝅗𝅥 = 1 beat. Thoughtfully.

Dear Lord Je - sus, Son of Ma - ry, List - en to our hum - ble prayer,

Help us all to be Thy chil - dren, Day by day and year by year.

Bless Thy Church, our homes, and fam - ily; Dear Lord Je - sus, hear our prayer. A - men.

Melody from *Danta De: Hymns to God, Ancient and*
Modern. Reprinted by permission of the Department of Education, Dublin.

Our Prayer

Oneida (N.Y.) Presbyterian Church School

BETTY M. GETMAN

♩ = 1 beat. Smoothly.

Be with us, Lord, in trou - ble; Be with us in our play.—

Help us, Lord, to wor - ship Thee And praise Thee ev - 'ry day. A - men.

Forgiveness

26

P

GEORGE WALLACE BRIGGS

JOHN DAY'S *Psalter*, 1562

♩ = 1 beat. Moderately slow.

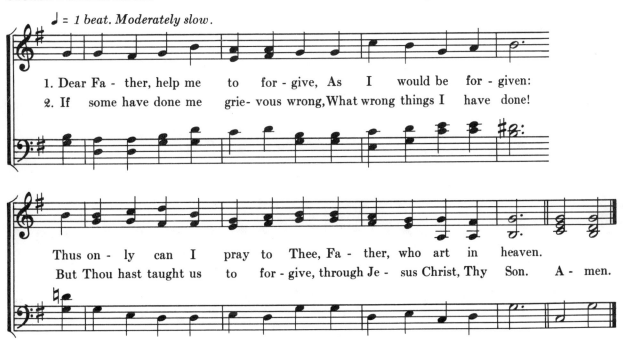

1. Dear Fa - ther, help me to for - give, As I would be for - given:
2. If some have done me grie- vous wrong, What wrong things I have done!

Thus on - ly can I pray to Thee, Fa - ther, who art in heaven.
But Thou hast taught us to for - give, through Je - sus Christ, Thy Son. A - men.

This melody, "St. Flavian," appears in *The Hymnal 1940* at #59, #198, #391, and #569.

27
K P

Forgive Me, God

An Episcopal Church School Class

Alt. from *The Revivalist*

Words from "Prayers for Boys and Girls," compiled by the Department of Christian Education of the Protestant Episcopal Church.

28
K

For the Things That I've Done Wrong

JOHN HARRELL

ORLANDO GIBBONS

This melody, "Song 13," appears in *The Hymnal 1940* at #451.

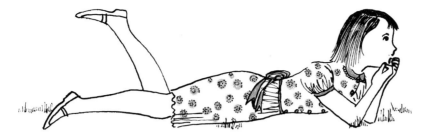

For other Lenten songs, see:

For a list of appropriate Lenten hymns in *The Hymnal 1940,* see page 132.

Palm Sunday

The Glory of Our King

29

K P

MARGARET B. CROPPER

Scottish Psalter

♩ = *1 beat. With dignity.*

1. The glo - ry of our King was seen When He came rid - ing by,
2. The glo - ry of our King was seen When, with His arms stretched wide,
3. The glo - ry of our King was seen On the first Eas - ter Day;

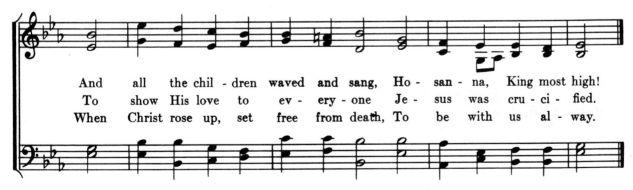

And all the chil - dren waved and sang, Ho - san - na, King most high!
To show His love to ev - ery - one Je - sus was cru - ci - fied.
When Christ rose up, set free from death, To be with us al - way.

Words of stanzas 1 and 2 reprinted by permission of the author, Margaret Cropper, from
Hymns and Songs for the Church Kindergarten. Words of stanza 3 © Margaret Cropper 1961.

This melody, "Dundee," appears in *The Hymnal 1940* at #397 and #497 and
elsewhere in this book at #54.

To Jesus Christ the Children Sang

30
P

ALDA M. MILNER-BARRY

Traditional.Cornish

♩. = *1 beat. Brightly.*

G ... D7 ... G ... D7

1. To Je - sus Christ_the chil - dren sang Ho - san - na, Lord!_ Ho - san - na!
2. To Je - sus Christ,_the chil - dren's King, Ho - san - na, Lord!_ Ho - san - na!

G ... C ... D7 ... G ... D7 ... G

Through_ ci - ty streets their voic - es rang, Ho - san - na, Lord! _ Ho - san - na!
With_ joy - ful hearts our praise_ we bring; Ho - san - na, Lord! _ Ho - san - na!

Words reprinted by permission of St. Christopher's College, London, England.

This melody appears elsewhere in this book at #34 and #48.

Riding, Riding

R. SOMERSET WARD

NORMAN AND MARGARET MEALY

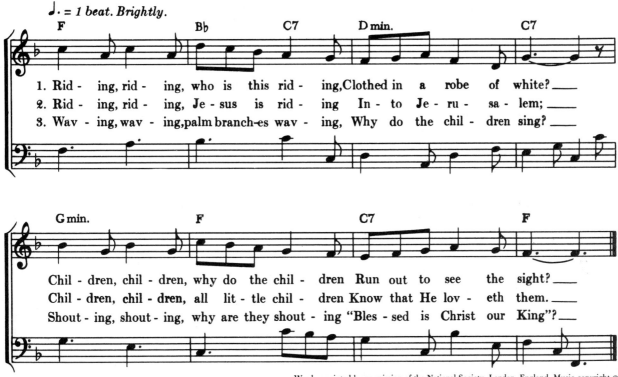

♩. = 1 beat. Brightly.

1. Rid - ing, rid - ing, who is this rid - ing, Clothed in a robe of white? ____
2. Rid - ing, rid - ing, Je - sus is rid - ing In - to Je - ru - sa - lem; ____
3. Wav - ing, wav - ing, palm branch-es wav - ing, Why do the chil - dren sing? ____

Chil - dren, chil - dren, why do the chil - dren Run out to see the sight? ____
Chil - dren, chil - dren, all lit - tle chil - dren Know that He lov - eth them. ____
Shout - ing, shout - ing, why are they shout - ing "Bles - sed is Christ our King"? ____

Words reprinted by permission of the National Society, London, England. Music copyright ©
The Seabury Press, Inc., 1955.

4. Waving, waving, children are waving
    Praise to the Son of God;
    Shouting, shouting, all of them shouting,
    "Welcome the children's Lord!"

The question-and-answer character of this song can be emphasized by having different children or groups sing alternate stanzas.

For a list of appropriate Palm Sunday hymns in *The Hymnal 1940*, see pages 132–133.

32

P

This Is the Day

Psalm 118:24

CHARLES CUSHING

♩ = 1 beat. Joyfully.

This is the day which the Lord hath made;

We will re- joice _____ and be glad in it.

smoothly

broadening

A small group of boys and girls can learn this song for a festive occasion or to sing regularly at the opening of services. Others will join in as the music becomes familiar to them.

28

Jesus Christ Is Ris'n Today

NORMAN AND MARGARET MEALY

Traditional Twelfth Century

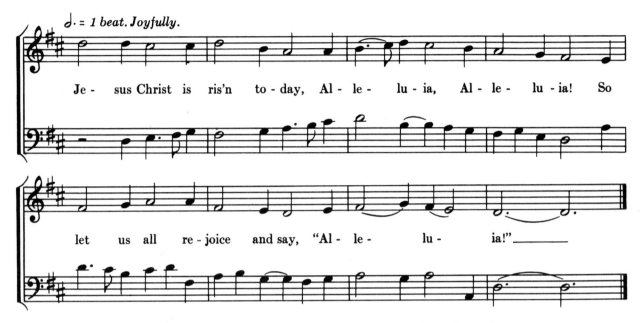

Je - sus Christ is ris'n to - day, Al - le - lu - ia, Al - le - lu - ia! So
let us all re - joice and say, "Al - le - lu - ia!"_____

It Is the Joyful Eastertime

ALDA M. MILNER-BARRY

Traditional Cornish

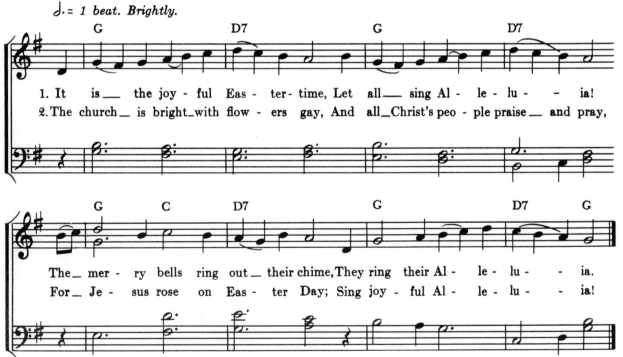

1. It   is___ the joy - ful Eas - ter - time, Let all___ sing Al - le - lu - ia!
2. The church_ is bright_with flow - ers gay, And all_Christ's peo - ple praise___ and pray,

The_ mer - ry bells ring out___ their chime, They ring their Al - le - lu - ia.
For_ Je - sus rose on Eas - ter Day; Sing joy - ful Al - le - lu - ia!

Words reprinted by permission of St. Christopher's College, London, England.

This melody appears elsewhere in this book at #30 and #48.

We Welcome Glad Easter

Unknown

Traditional Welsh

1. We wel - come glad Eas - ter when Je - sus our Lord
2. And tell how three Ma - rys came ear - ly that day
3. And sing of the an - gel who said: "Do not fear!"

A - rose from the dead ___ to live ev - er - more.
And found at the tomb ___ the stone rolled a - way.
Your Sa - viour is ri - sen; He is not here."

Then raise joy - ful voi - ces, ye chil - dren, and sing,

Bring glad Eas - ter prais - es to Je - sus, our King.

Words (alt.) reprinted by permission of Concordia Publishing House, St. Louis, Mo.

This melody, "St. Denio," appears in *The Hymnal 1940* at #301.

Good Joseph Had a Garden

ALDA M. MILNER-BARRY   Traditional English

♩ = 1 beat. With spirit.

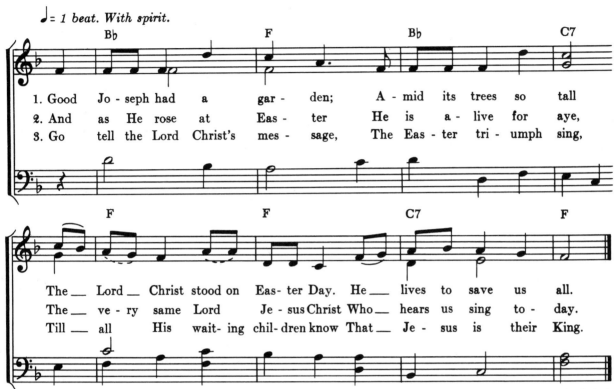

1. Good Jo - seph had a   gar - den;   A - mid its trees so   tall
2. And   as He rose at   Eas - ter   He is a - live for   aye,
3. Go   tell the Lord Christ's mes - sage,   The Eas - ter tri - umph sing,

The __ Lord __ Christ stood on Eas - ter Day. He __ lives to save us   all.
The __ ve - ry same Lord   Je - sus Christ Who __ hears us sing to - day.
Till __ all   His   wait- ing chil- dren know That __ Je - sus is   their King.

Words reprinted by permission of St. Christopher's College, London, England.

Explain, if necessary, that Joseph of Arimathea is not the Joseph of the Christmas
story. Pronounce "aye," which means "always," to rhyme with "day."

31

37
NK

Happy Easter Morning

JOHN HARRELL   JOHN HARRELL

♩ = 1 beat. Brightly.

G   D7   G

Hap - py Eas - ter morn - ing, Ev - ery - one is sing - ing,

A min.   D7   G   D7   G

Joy - ful bells are ring - ing: Hap - py Eas - ter day.

By substituting the word "Christmas" for "Easter," this becomes a Christmas song. Children may use triangles to make the sound of ringing bells.

38
KP

We Will Be Merry

Fourteenth or Fifteenth Century   MICHAEL PRAETORIUS
German, alt.   Ed. by W. LAWRENCE CURRY

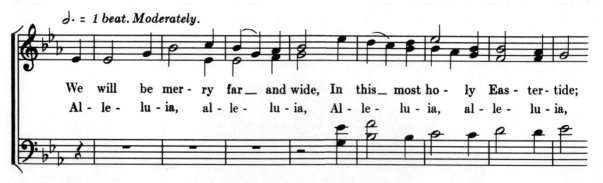

♩. = 1 beat. Moderately.

We will be mer - ry far _ and wide, In this _ most ho - ly Eas - ter - tide;
Al - le - lu - ia, al - le - lu - ia, Al - le - lu - ia, al - le - lu - ia,

Sing al - le - lu - ia to our Lord.
Sing al - le - lu - ia to our Lord.

Christ Our Lord Is Risen

NORMAN AND MARGARET MEALY

Traditional American

Christ our Lord is ri - sen, Christ our Lord is ri - sen.

Christ our Lord is ri - sen, and lives for - ev - er - more, and

lives for - ev - er - more, and lives for - ev - er - more;

Christ our Lord is ri - sen and lives for - ev - er - more.

Melody from *American Folk Songs for Children* by Ruth Crawford Seeger, published by
Doubleday & Company; reprinted by permission of Charles Seeger.

Children in the kindergarten or primary grades can make up other verses about
the Easter story, using the same refrain, "and lives forevermore." Two such
verses might be, "He rose on Easter morning . . . ," and "He came to His
disciples . . ."

This melody also appears at #12 with Christmas words.

40

P

Hail His Name

LOUIS F. BENSON   Traditional English

♩ = 1 beat. With spirit.

Hail His Name, ye moun - tains, And with it, val - leys, ring;

Leap for joy, ye foun - tains, A - mong the hills, __ and sing,

"Joy! be - hold He liv - eth, He liv - eth who was __ dead;

Christ our gra - cious Sav - iour Is ris - en, as __ He said."

An Easter Carol

CHRISTINA ROSSETTI

Based on Traditional Dutch

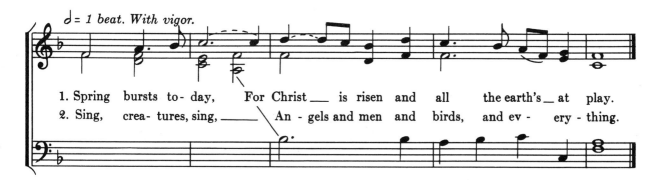

1. Spring bursts to-day, For Christ __ is risen and all the earth's __ at play.
2. Sing, crea-tures, sing, _____ An - gels and men and birds, and ev - ery - thing.

Gloria, Gloria

NORMAN AND MARGARET MEALY

Traditional Russian

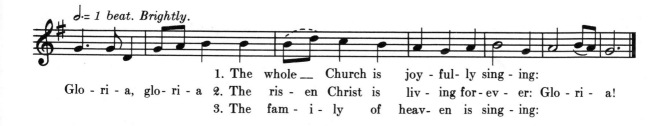

1. The whole __ Church is joy-ful-ly sing-ing:

Glo - ri - a, glo - ri - a 2. The ris - en Christ is liv - ing for-ev - er: Glo - ri - a!

3. The fam - i - ly of heav - en is sing - ing:

The Lark Sings Loud

Tr. from Russian by EDITH CLEGG, alt.

A. S. ARENSKY (melody)

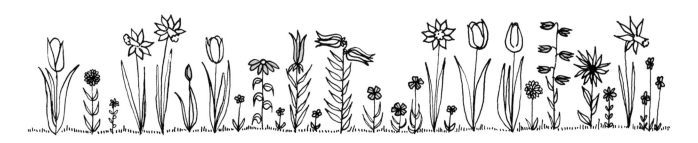

And ev'-ry-thing gives back the cry, "Re - joice now Christ is ris - en!"

After listening to this song a few times, children can join in and sing the recurring words, "Christ is risen." Later they may sing the whole phrase, "Rejoice now Christ is risen," and next the entire last line. Finally, they will learn the whole song.

Every Sunday is a celebration of Christ's resurrection; thus the following Easter hymns can well be used throughout the year:

32	This Is the Day	P
33	Jesus Christ Is Ris'n Today	K P
36	Good Joseph Had a Garden (stanza 2, beginning "As Jesus rose," and stanza 3)	P
39	Christ Our Lord Is Risen	N K P
40	Hail His Name	P
42	Gloria, Gloria	K P

For other Easter songs, see:

29	The Glory of Our King (stanza 3)	K P
57	The Sunday [Easter] Bells Are Ringing (see note)	N K
151	We're Making Valentines [coloring Easter eggs] (see note)	N K

For a list of appropriate Easter hymns in *The Hymnal 1940*, see page 133.

For Rogation songs, see:

103	When the Wheat Is Planted	P
105	Look! Look! Our Seeds We're Planting	N K

For a Rogation hymn in *The Hymnal 1940*, see:

138	"We plow the fields, and scatter" (refrain)	N K
	(stanza 1)	P

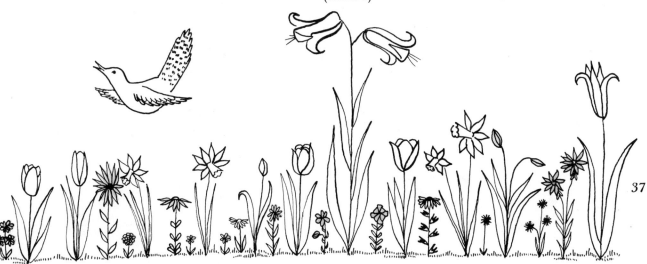

44
P

Christ the King

F. ABAIR

Tone VIII

Joyously, in flowing style.

1. Christ shall rule in ma - jes - ty Men and an - gels might - i - ly.
2. Christ shall rule e - ter - nal - ly O - ver sky and land and sea.

All the na - tions shall a - dore Christ, the King, for - ev - er - more!
Shout the word from shore to shore: "Christ the King for - ev - er - more!"

See page 131 for suggestions about singing and accompanying plainsong.

38

May the Gospel of the Lord

S. N. SEDGWICK

JUSTIN HEINRICH KNECHT

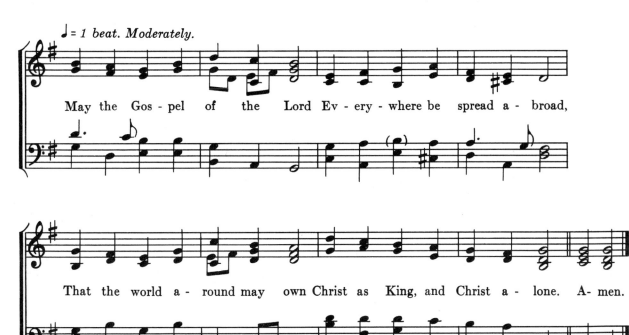

May the Gos-pel of the Lord Ev-ery-where be spread a-broad,

That the world a-round may own Christ as King, and Christ a-lone. A-men.

This melody, "Vienna," appears in *The Hymnal 1940* at #239.

Gloria, Gloria

NORMAN AND MARGARET MEALY

Traditional Russian

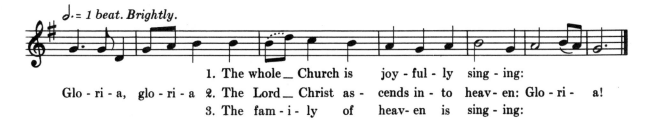

1. The whole Church is joy-ful-ly sing-ing:
Glo-ri-a, glo-ri-a 2. The Lord Christ as-cends in-to heav-en: Glo-ri-a!
3. The fam-i-ly of heav-en is sing-ing:

For another Ascension song, see:
18   From East to West   P

For a list of appropriate Ascension hymns in *The Hymnal 1940*, see page 133.

The Coming of the Spirit

F. ABAIR

Plainsong

In a narrative style.

1. The wind was loud, all men could hear. It was the Spir-it com-ing near.
2. The doors the A -pos - tles o - pened wide And preached to all the crowds out - side.
3. The Spir - it gave the power to each In ma - ny lan - gua - ges to preach.

In flames of fire so gleam - ing red He shone on each A - pos - tle's head.
Their hearts were brave, their minds were clear, They had no doubt nor a - ny fear.
And those who heard them knelt to pray. Three thou-sand were bap - tized __ that day.

This melody, "Splendor Paternae," appears in *The Hymnal 1940* at # 158. See
page 131 for suggestions about singing and accompanying plainsong.

It Is the Holy Spirit's Day

48
P

ALDA M. MILNER-BARRY

Traditional Cornish

1. It is __ the Ho - ly Spi - rit's day, Sing joy - ful Al - le - lu - ia!
2. With rush - ing sound, with heav'n - ly flame On them __ the Ho - ly Spi - rit came:

When __ all Christ's peo - ple met __ to pray; Sing joy - ful Al - le - lu - ia!
They __ blessed and praised God's glo - rious name; Sing joy - ful Al - le - lu - ia!

Words reprinted by permission of St. Christopher's College, London, England.

This melody appears elsewhere in this book at #30 and #34.

Gloria, Gloria

49
K P

NORMAN AND MARGARET MEALY

Traditional Russian

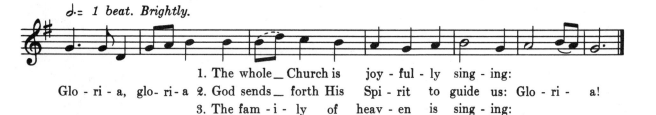

1. The whole __ Church is joy - ful - ly sing - ing:
Glo - ri - a, glo - ri - a 2. God sends __ forth His Spi - rit to guide us: Glo - ri - a!
3. The fam - i - ly of heav - en is sing - ing:

For another Whitsunday song, see:

93 Who Has Seen the Wind? N K

For a list of appropriate Whitsunday hymns in *The Hymnal 1940,* see page 133.

50

P

Sing to Our God

MARGARET B. CROPPER

Traditional Welsh

♩ = 1 beat. Sturdily.

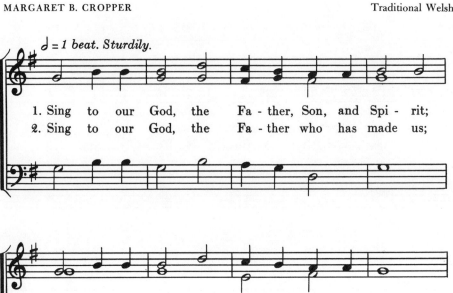

1. Sing to our God, the Fa - ther, Son, and Spi - rit;
2. Sing to our God, the Fa - ther who has made us;

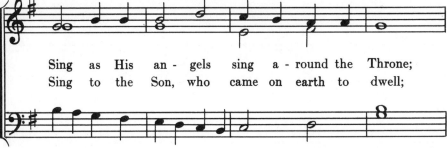

Sing as His an - gels sing a - round the Throne;
Sing to the Son, who came on earth to dwell;

Sing, Chil - dren, God is near us and He loves us;
Sing to the Spi - rit, help - ing all the chil - dren;

Sing Ho - ly, Ho - ly, Ho - ly, ev - ery - one.
Sing songs of love, and joy - ful prais - es tell.

42

Words reprinted by permission of the author.

God, the Father, Bless Us

Unknown   CASPAR ETT

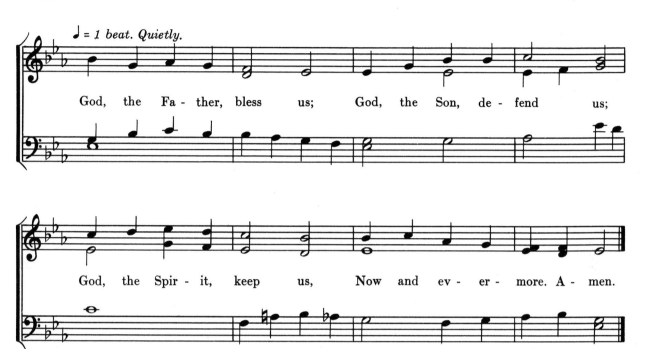

God, the Fa - ther, bless us; God, the Son, de - fend us;

God, the Spir - it, keep us, Now and ev - er - more. A - men.

Words and melody reprinted by permission of Concordia Publishing House, St. Louis, Mo.

For a list of appropriate Trinity hymns in *The Hymnal 1940,* see page 133.

Saints' Days

Gloria, Gloria

52

K P

NORMAN AND MARGARET MEALY   Traditional Russian

1. The whole__ Church is   joy - ful - ly   sing - ing:
Glo - ri - a,   Glo - ri - a 2. All   saints__   join   in   prais - ing their Mak - er: Glo - ri - a!
                              3. The   fam - i - ly   of   heav - en is   sing - ing:

43

53
P

Brave Men

VICTORIA SAFFELLE JOHNSON

HOWARD C. ROBBINS
Har. by RAY F. BROWN

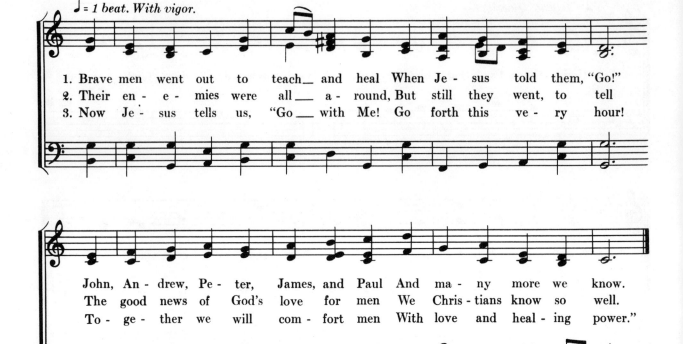

♩ = 1 beat. With vigor.

1. Brave men went out to teach__ and heal When Je - sus told them, "Go!"
2. Their en - e - mies were all __ a - round, But still they went, to tell
3. Now Je - sus tells us, "Go __ with Me! Go forth this ve - ry hour!

John, An - drew, Pe - ter, James, and Paul And ma - ny more we know.
The good news of God's love for men We Chris - tians know so well.
To - ge - ther we will com - fort men With love and heal - ing power."

Words © Victoria Saffelle Johnson 1961. Music reprinted by permission of The Church Pension Fund.

This melody, "Chelsea Square," appears in *The Hymnal 1940* at #380.

For other songs for saints' days, see:

For a list of appropriate hymns for saints' days in *The Hymnal 1940*, see page 134.

44

The Church the Family of God

GEORGE WALLACE BRIGGS

Scottish Psalter

♩ = 1 beat. Thoughtfully.

1. The Church is God's great fam - i - ly, And I a mem - ber am:
2. Though scat - tered o - ver all the world, Of ev - ery race and land,

My bro - thers and my sis - ters all Who bear Christ's ho - ly Name.
One Name we bear, one faith pro - claim, One fam - i - ly we stand.

This melody, "Dundee," appears in *The Hymnal 1940* at #397 and #497, and elsewhere in this book at #29.

55
KP

Baptized with Water

VICTORIA SAFFELLE JOHNSON

Est's *Whole Book of Psalmes*

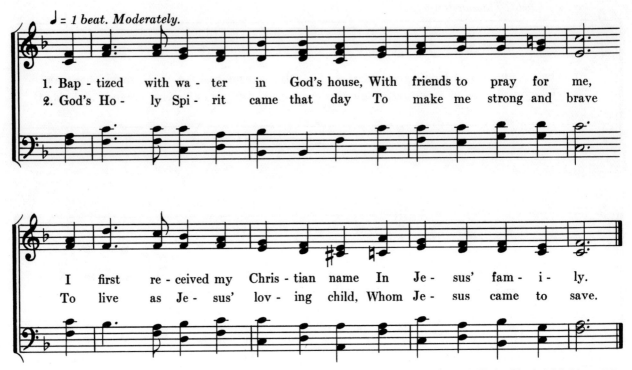

♩ = 1 beat. Moderately.

1. Bap - tized with wa - ter in God's house, With friends to pray for me,
2. God's Ho - ly Spi - rit came that day To make me strong and brave

I first re - ceived my Chris - tian name In Je - sus' fam - i - ly.
To live as Je - sus' lov - ing child, Whom Je - sus came to save.

Words © Victoria Saffelle Johnson 1961.

This melody, "Winchester Old," appears in *The Hymnal 1940* at #13.

For a Baptism hymn in *The Hymnal 1940*, see page 134.

They Healed the Sick

VICTORIA SAFFELLE JOHNSON

W. A. GOLDSWORTHY

1. They healed the sick in Je-sus' Name John, Pe-ter, James, and Paul,
2. Now priests and bish-ops in God's Church, Who work on earth to-day,
3. I, too, have work to do for God. Bap-tized in-to His grace,

A-pos-tles whom our Sa-viour sent To bring His joy to all.
With ho-ly oil a-noint the sick, And for each one they pray.
I pray to Him for those I love, Both here and ev-ery place.

This melody, "Bouwerie," appears in *The Hymnal 1940* at #330.

The Sunday Bells Are Ringing

57

N K

E.M., alt.

Traditional French

♩. = 1 beat. With vigor.

A min.   E7   A min.   E7   A min.

The Sun - day bells are ring - ing, A ding a ding a ding;____

A min.   E7   A min.   E7   A min.

Come all good Chris - tian peo - ple, O come to Church and sing.____

E7   A min.   A min.   E7   A min.

Come fa - thers all and mo - thers, Come sis - ters and come bro - thers,

48

A min.   E7   A min.   E7   A min.

The Sun - day bells are ring - ing, A ding a ding a ding._____

8 va -

Let the children sway like bells, pretend to pull bell ropes, or strike triangles while they sing. For very small children, use only the first one or two lines. "Easter" or "Christmas" may be substituted for "Sunday," or sing the name of your own town ("The Berkeley bells . . . ," "Chicago bells . . . .").

Who Rings the Bell?

58

K

Stanza 1: AGNES LECKIE MASON
Stanza 2: NORMAN AND MARGARET MEALY

PHYLLIS BROWN OHANIAN

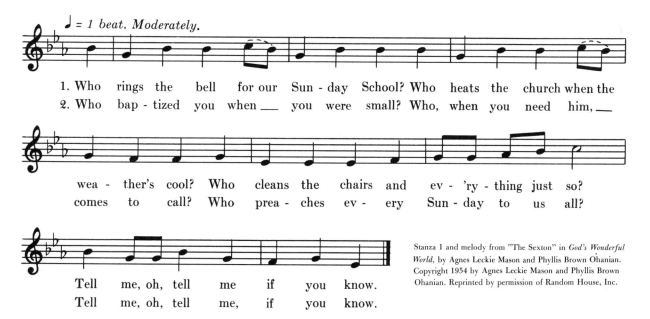

♩ = 1 beat. Moderately.

1. Who rings the bell for our Sun - day School? Who heats the church when the
2. Who bap - tized you when ___ you were small? Who, when you need him, ___

wea - ther's cool? Who cleans the chairs and ev - 'ry - thing just so?
comes to call? Who prea - ches ev - ery Sun - day to us all?

Stanza 1 and melody from "The Sexton" in *God's Wonderful World*, by Agnes Leckie Mason and Phyllis Brown Ohanian. Copyright 1954 by Agnes Leckie Mason and Phyllis Brown Ohanian. Reprinted by permission of Random House, Inc.

Tell me, oh, tell me if you know.
Tell me, oh, tell me, if you know.

Make up other verses describing the work of a church school teacher, an organist, etc. Rhyming is not necessary. Children may want to *sing* an answer with their own tune.

59
KP

I Was Glad

Psalm 122:1

BARBARA CLUTE

♪ = 1 beat. With solemn joy.

I was _____ glad when they said un - to me,

We will _ go in - to the house of _ the Lord.

60
N

D.W.   D.W.

Ding Dong!

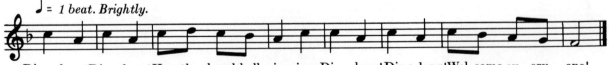

♩ = 1 beat. Brightly.

Ding, dong! Ding, dong! Hear the church bells ring-ing: Ding, dong! Ding, dong! Wel- come, ev - ery - one!

For other songs about the Church, see:
24   Dear Lord Jesus   P
42, 46, 49, 52   Gloria, Gloria   K P

With songs of praise we lift our hearts
in gratitude for all God's gifts,
and especially for His redeeming grace.

O Ye Children of Men,

Bless Ye the Lord

PRAISE AND THANKSGIVING

THANKS FOR SPECIAL THINGS

GRACES

Benedicite

61
P

From *Song of the Three Holy Children*

Anglican Chant
T. TERTIUS NOBLE, alt.

1. O all ye Pow - ers of the Lord,
3. O ye Moun - tains and Hills,
5. O ye Chil - dren of Men,

bless ye the Lord:

praise Him, and mag - ni - fy Him for ev - - er.

2. O ye Sun and Moon,
4. O ye Seas and Floods,

bless ye the Lord:

6. Let us bless the Fa - ther, and the Son, and the Ho - ly Ghost:

praise Him, and mag - ni - fy Him for ev - - er.

Sing the Benedicite as you would read it aloud. Let the rhythm be that of the words; the notes have no definite time value in chanting. Here are four different ways to sing the Benedicite:

1. Some sing the verses, others sing the refrain ("praise Him . . .").
2. Some sing the odd-numbered verses and refrain, others answer with the even-numbered verses and refrain.
3. One person sings each verse, everyone sings the refrain.
4. Children take turns singing the verses alone, everyone sings the refrain.

Other verses from the Benedicite may be added in pairs. This song may be useful for an offertory procession at the Eucharist.

62

KP

Praise and Thanksgiving

German
Adapted by EDITH LOVELL THOMAS

Traditional Alsatian

Words and melody from *The Whole World Singing*, edited by Edith Lovell Thomas; reprinted by permission of Friendship Press, Inc.

This song can be sung as a round. For directions, see page 129.

63
NKP

Help Our Lips to Praise Thee

RUTH IRWIN REX   JOHN HARRELL

♩ = 1 beat. Quietly.

Help our lips to praise Thee;

Help our hands to serve Thee;

Help our hearts to love Thee. A - men.

Words reprinted by permission of author and Fleming H. Revell Company.

64
KP

Praise to the Lord

JOACHIM NEANDER
Tr. CATHERINE WINKWORTH, alt.

Stralsund Gesangbuch

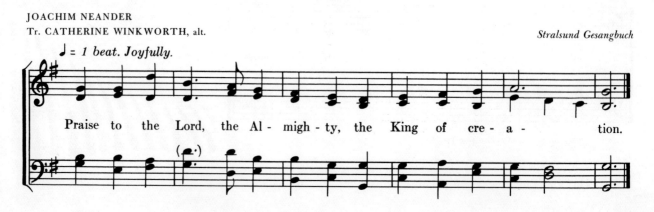

♩ = 1 beat. Joyfully.

Praise to the Lord, the Al - migh - ty, the King of cre - a - tion.

54

This is part of the melody "Praise to the Lord," which appears in *The Hymnal 1940* at #279.

Thank You, God, for Everything

Second-Grade Children
Riverside Church, N.Y.C.

Second-Grade Children
Riverside Church, N.Y.C.

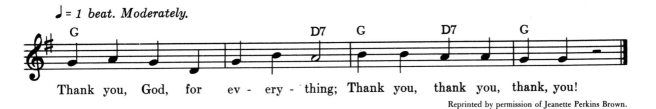

Thank you, God, for ev - ery - thing; Thank you, thank you, thank, you!

Now Thank We All Our God

MARTIN RINKART
Tr. CATHERINE WINKWORTH, alt.

JOHANN CRUEGER

Now thank we all our God, With heart, and hands, and voic - es.

Primary children can sing the entire first stanza of this hymn, #276 in *The Hymnal 1940*. The melody, "Nun danket," also appears in *The Hymnal 1940* at #144.

The Lord Has Done Great Things

Graded Rounds and Catches

Adapted from Psalm 126

The Lord has done great things for us, and we are ve - ry glad.

Children can make up other appropriate verses, such as, "The Lord has sent His Son to us, and we are very glad." This song can be sung as a round, without the Autoharp chords. For directions, see page 129.

68

NKP

All Good Gifts Around Us

MATTHIAS CLAUDIUS
Tr. JANE M. CAMPBELL

J. A. P. SCHULZ

♩ = 1 beat. With energy.

All good gifts a-round us Are sent from heav'n a-bove;

Then thank the Lord, O thank the Lord For all His love.

This is the refrain of the melody "Claudius," which appears in *The Hymnal 1940* at #138.

69

KP

Give Praise and Glory

J. J. SCHUETZ
Tr. ARTHUR W. FARLANDER and WINFRED DOUGLAS

PETER SOHREN

♩ = 1 beat. Joyously.

Give praise and glo-ry un-to God, The Fa-ther of all bless-ing.

Translation reprinted by permission of The Church Pension Fund.

This is part of the melody "Elbing," which appears in *The Hymnal 1940* at #287 and #299.

For other general songs of praise, see the suggestions on page 37 and:

18	From East to West	P
44	Christ the King	P
50	Sing to Our God	P
74	Evening Prayer Hymn	P
81	All Creatures of Our God and King	P

For a list of appropriate hymns of praise and thanksgiving in *The Hymnal 1940*, see pages 133–134.

Service music may also be used, for example, the Venite, Jubilate Deo, Gloria Patri, Sanctus, and Gloria in excelsis. See page 135.

A Thank You Prayer

EMILIE FENDALL JOHNSON

Traditional Welsh

♩ = 1 beat. Moderately.

Dear _ Lord, we give thanks for the bright si - lent moon,

And _ thanks for the sun that will warm us at noon.

And _ thanks for the stars and the quick-run - ning breeze,

And _ thanks for the shade and the straight-ness of trees.

71

KP

We Thank Thee, God, for Hands to Feel

F. ELLENORE PRINCE

Melody alt. from J. A. P. SCHULZ

♩ = 1 beat. Moderately.

F   Bb   F

We __ thank Thee, God, for hands to feel,

F   Bb   F

For __ legs to run and climb and kneel,

Bb   C7   F

For __ feet that car - ry us all day

Bb   C7   F

While we're at work, and while   at   play.   A - men.

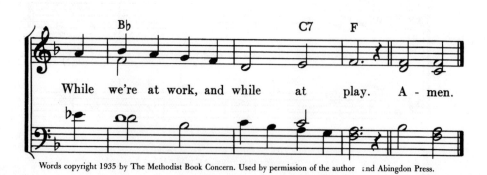

For Little Things

MARGARET CLEMENS   Traditional English

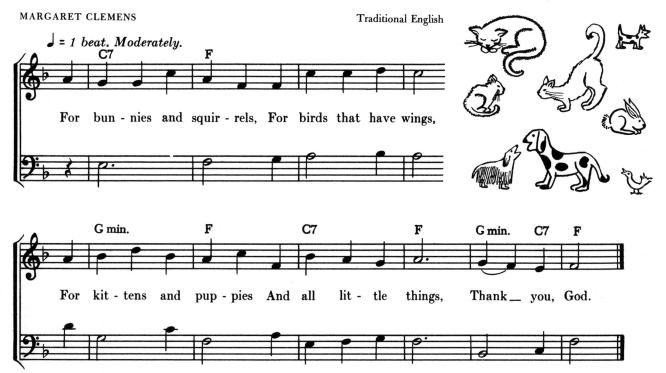

♩ = 1 beat. Moderately.

For bun - nies and squir - rels, For birds that have wings,

For kit - tens and pup - pies And all lit - tle things, Thank_ you, God.

Words from *My Prayer Book* by Margaret Clemens. Copyright 1947 by Rand McNally & Company, publishers. Melody, "Hardwick" (slightly altered), taken from *Songs of Praise* (Enlarged Edition) by permission of the Oxford University Press, London, England.

We Are Glad for Apples

Unknown   D. W.

♩ = 1 beat. Cheerfully.

We are glad for ap - ples, We are glad for ap - ples. Thank you, God.

Words used by the Nursery Department of St. Alban's Episcopal Church, Los Angeles, Calif.

Change "apples" to suit special occasions: "crayons," "sunshine," "Easter," "Mr. ——," etc. For songs of this type, children can make up tunes of their own as well as words.

Evening Prayer Hymn

74
P

Japanese
Tr. BESSIE McKIM and DOROTHY STOUT, alt.

T. S. TYNG

♩ = 1 beat. Slowly, without dragging.

Fa- ther, through this day Un - der thy al - migh - ty care

We have lived in peace. Now we sing a joy - ful prayer

Giv - ing praise and thanks to thee. A - men.

Words and melody reprinted by permission of the Department of Archives and Documents
of the National Council of the Nippon Seikokai, copyright owners.

Some Things We Are Specially Glad About

Church School Children, Roanridge, Missouri, alt.

Adapted from the ancient setting of the Litany

Thoughtfully.

1. For the light for my work and my play,
2. For the dark for my sleep, Thank you, Heav'n-ly Fa - ther.
3. For my fam - i - ly and friends who care for me,

4. For all the animals that play with me, ... 5. For all your love by night and day, ...

Words from "O Come, Let Us Worship," compiled by The National Town-Country Church Institute of the Protestant Episcopal Church.

Sing this as you would read it aloud. Let the rhythm be that of the words; the notes have no definite time value in chanting. No accompaniment is needed. This song needs to be sung with the teacher or individual children singing the verses and the group joining in on the response. On this model a class can make up its own "litany." Parents may find this useful as a child's bedtime prayer.

Graces

For Health and Strength

Traditional

Graded Rounds and Catches

♩ = 1 beat. *Moderately.*

For health and strength and dai - ly food, We praise Thy name, O Lord.

Melody reprinted by permission of J. Curwen & Sons, Ltd.

You can sing this as a round, without the Autoharp chords. (Directions for singing rounds are on page 129.)

Thank You, God, for Milk and Bread

ELIZABETH McE. SHIELDS

Traditional English

𝅗𝅥 = 1 beat. *Thoughtfully.*

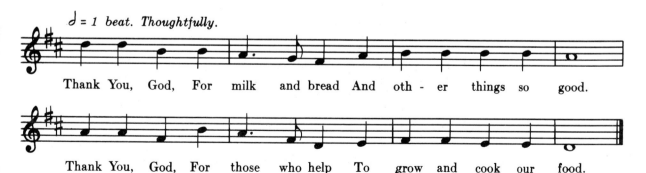

Thank You, God, For milk and bread And oth - er things so good.

Thank You, God, For those who help To grow and cook our food.

Words from *Prayers for Little Children*, edited by Mary Alice Jones. Copyright 1937 by Rand McNally & Company, publishers. Melody, "St. Hugh" (slightly altered), taken from *The English Hymnal* by permission of the Oxford University Press, London, England.

Graces

78 — God Is Great and God Is Good

N K

Traditional

CONRAD KOCHER

God is great and God is good, And we thank Him for our food. A - men.

This is the refrain from the melody "Dix," which appears in *The Hymnal 1940* at #52 and #140.

79 — To God Who Gives Us Daily Bread

K P

M. RUMSEY

ORLANDO GIBBONS

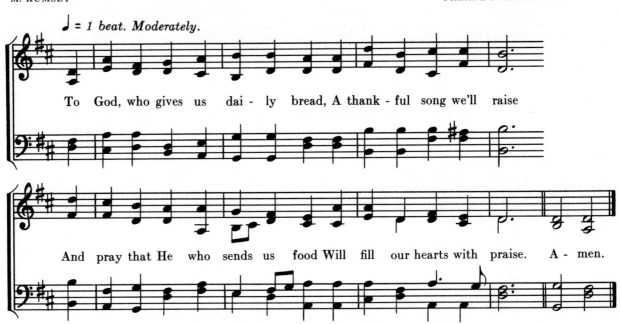

To God, who gives us dai - ly bread, A thank - ful song we'll raise

And pray that He who sends us food Will fill our hearts with praise. A - men.

This melody, "Song 67," appears in *The Hymnal 1940* at #404.

For other graces and songs of special thanks, see:

62	Praise and Thanksgiving	K P
65	Thank You, God, for Everything	N K
66	Now Thank We All Our God	N K
68	All Good Gifts Around Us	N K P
83	God Made the Sun	N K
84	God Made the Tiny Freckled Fish	P
86	My Place in God's World	P
103	When the Wheat Is Planted	P
108	Thanks for Meadows	N K P
122	Good Morning, God, Now It Is Light	N K
139	Birthday Song	N K P

For a list of hymns of special thanks in *The Hymnal 1940*, see page 134.

For a grace from *The Hymnal 1940*, see:

139	"Praise God, from whom all blessings flow"	K P

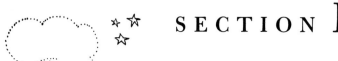

For thousands of years the children of
God have sung of His wonderful world.
"Let the heavens be glad, and let the earth rejoice."
So we, too, sing of wind and stars, of
freckled fish, of the glory of God's creation.

Heaven and Earth

Are Full of Thy Glory

GOD THE CREATOR

BIRDS, BUGS, AND BEASTS

WHERE AND WHY

WEATHER AND SEASONS

O Father, the Maker of Beautiful Things

80

K P

PERCY DEARMER, alt.

Melody alt. from *Slave Songs of the United States*

♩ = 1 beat. Brightly.

1. O Fa - ther, the mak - er of beau - ti - ful things,
2. All crea - tures are thine in the world and be - yond,

Like ros - es and_ dai - sies and but - ter - flies' wings,
The bee in the_ pol - len, the fish in the pond,

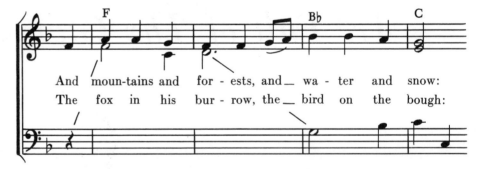

And moun - tains and for - ests, and_ wa - ter and snow:
The fox in his bur - row, the_ bird on the bough:

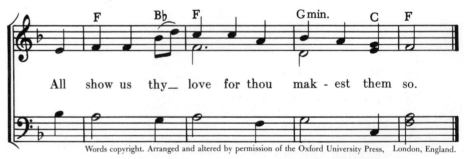

All show us thy_ love for thou mak - est them so.

Words copyright. Arranged and altered by permission of the Oxford University Press,   London, England.

3. The lambs and the calves and the foals that are born,
   The beans and potatoes, the roots and the corn,
   The apple and cherry trees, row after row:
   All show us thy love for thou makest them so.

A teacher or parent may sing the stanzas, the children joining in the refrain, "All show us. . . ." Children can draw, paint, or make posters (using cut-out pictures) of the many things mentioned in the song.

All Creatures of Our God and King

81

P

ST. FRANCIS OF ASSISI
Tr. by WILLIAM H. DRAPER

Cologne *Gesangbuch*

♩ = 1 beat. Joyfully, with dignity.

(A)   (B)

1. All crea-tures of our God and King,   Lift up your voice and with us sing
2. Thou flow-ing wa-ter, pure and clear,   Make mu-sic for thy Lord to hear,

(A)   (B)

Al - le - lu - ia, al - le - lu - ia!

(A)   (B)

Thou burn-ing sun with gol- den beam,   Thou sil- ver moon with sof- ter gleam,
Thou fire so mas- ter-ful and bright,   That giv- est man both warmth and light,

(A)   (B)   (A)   (B)   (A and B)

O __ praise Him, O __ praise Him, Al-le - lu - ia, al - le - lu - ia, al - le - lu - ia!

Words from Curwen Edition No. 80649; reprinted by permission of J. Curwen & Sons, Ltd.

At first, the children can sing the "Alleluias" and the refrain "O praise Him. . . ."
Later, they can divide in two groups and echo each other on the refrain (as indicated by "A" and "B" on the music). When they are familiar with the whole
song, the two groups can sing alternate phrases throughout (following "A" and
"B"). Or, individual children can take turns singing the verses, with everyone
joining on the "Alleluias" and refrain.

This melody, "Vigiles et sancti," appears in *The Hymnal 1940* at #599.

82

Who Made the Stars

MIRIAM DRURY

MIRIAM DRURY

♩. = 1 beat. With movement.

1. Who made the stars in the wide blue sky?
2. Who made the flowers and trees to grow? God our Father.
3. Who made the peo - ple — ev - 'ry - where?

Who made the bees and birds that fly?
Who made the rain - drops and the snow? God our lov - ing Fa - ther.
Who gives to all His love and care?

Words and melody from *When the Little Child Wants to Sing*. Copyright, 1935, by the Presbyterian Board of Christian Education. Used by permission.

Children will quickly learn the "answer" part. Later, they can make up other questions for verses. Rhyming is not necessary.

83

God Made the Sun

LEAH GALE, alt.   Traditional French

♩. = 1 beat. Moderately.

God made the sun   And God made the tree,

God made the moun - tains And God   made me.

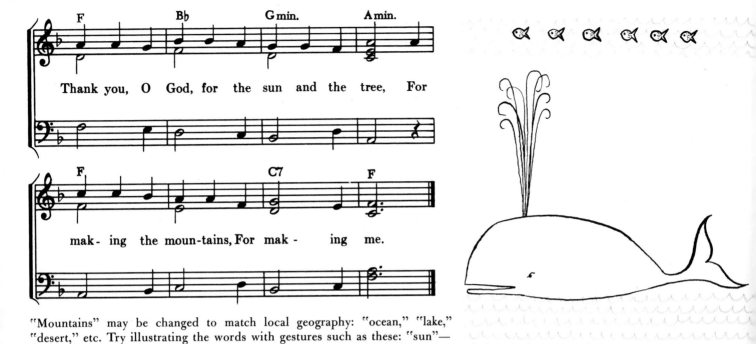

Thank you, O God, for the sun and the tree, For mak-ing the moun-tains, For mak- ing me.

"Mountains" may be changed to match local geography: "ocean," "lake," "desert," etc. Try illustrating the words with gestures such as these: "sun"—make a circle with both arms reaching up; "tree"—stretch arms out sideways; "mountains"—put both arms up and touch fingertips to make a "peak"; "me"—point to self.

84
P

God Made the Tiny Freckled Fish

CAROL CHRISTOPHER DRAKE

Southern Harmony

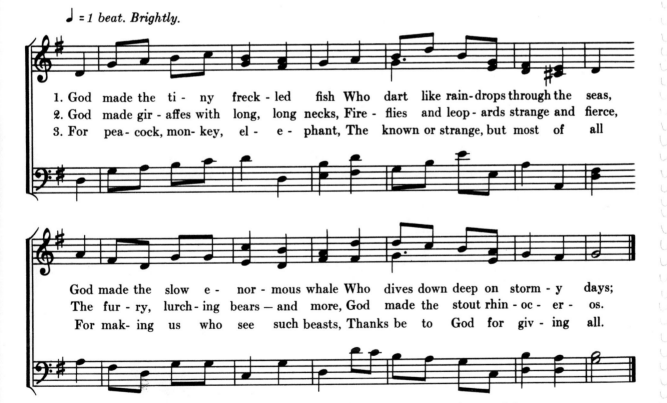

♩ = 1 beat. *Brightly.*

1. God made the ti - ny freck - led fish Who dart like rain-drops through the seas,
2. God made gir - affes with long, long necks, Fire - flies and leop - ards strange and fierce,
3. For pea - cock, mon - key, el - e - phant, The known or strange, but most of all

God made the slow e - nor - mous whale Who dives down deep on storm - y days;
The fur - ry, lurch - ing bears — and more, God made the stout rhin - oc - er - os.
For mak - ing us who see such beasts, Thanks be to God for giv - ing all.

Here is a song to start children talking or drawing pictures of some of the surprising creatures in God's world.

67

85
KP

God Speaks to Us in All We Know

CAROL CHRISTOPHER DRAKE

The Vestry Harp

God speaks to ___ us in all ___ we know, Through an - y ___ way we will hear:

The birds, the ___ rain, the mor - ning ___ sun Tell ___ all who will that God is here.

86
P

My Place in God's World

NORMAN AND MARGARET MEALY

Traditional English

1. God who put the stars in space, Who made the world we share,
2. Thank You, God, for stars in space And for the world we share.

In His mak - ing made a place For me, and put me here.
Thank You for my spec - ial place To love and serve You here. A - men.

Words based on a poem by Lucile S. Reed and the ideas of her second-grade class. Melody, "Mendip" (slightly altered), taken from *Songs of Praise* (Enlarged Edition) by permission of the Oxford University Press, London, England.

The Squirrel

Unknown

Traditional Latin American

1. Whis - ky, fris - ky. Hip - pi - ty hop; Up____ he goes _____ To the tree top!
2. Whirl - y, twirl - y, Round____ and round, Down ___ he scam - pers To ___ the ground.
3. Furl - y, curl - y, What ___ a tail! Tall as a fea - ther, Broad as a sail!
4. Where's his sup - per? In ____ the shell, Snap - pi - ty, crack - i - ty, Out ___ it fell.

Homes

ELEANOR DOAN

NORMAN AND MARGARET MEALY

Rab - bits have homes—The holes they build; Bears have homes—Caves in the hill;
(L.H. make hole) (L.H. make semi-circular "cave" on back of R.H.)

Ants have homes— A mound of dirt; Go - phers have homes — In the earth;
(R.H. cupped like hill, on palm of L.H.) (R. index finger goes into hole formed by L.H.)

Birds have homes—Nests in trees; And God told them all How to build these.____
(Hands cupped together for "nest")

Words reprinted from *Fascinating Finger Fun*, by Eleanor Doan, by permission from the
Zondervan Publishing House, Grand Rapids, Mich.

My Kitty

HELEN BAYLEY DAVIS, alt.

Traditional German

1. My kit-ty has a lit-tle song She hums in-side of her;
2. It sounds just like she's wind-ing up A tin-y clock she keeps

She curls up by__ the kit-chen stove And then be-gins to purr.
In-side her beaut-i-ful fur__ coat To wake her, when she sleeps.

Words from *The Christian Advocate*. Original title, "Song for a Child."

O Cow, O Cow, What Use Are You?

SATIS N. COLEMAN and ALICE G. THORN

SATIS N. COLEMAN and ALICE G. THORN

1. O cow, O cow, what use are you? "I give you good milk and that's what I do."
2. O sheep, O sheep, what use are you? "I give you warm wool and that's what I do."

From *Singing Time*, published by The John Day Company. Copyright 1929 by Satis N. Coleman and Alice G. Thorn.

3. O hen, O hen . . . "I lay you good eggs . . ."
4. O pony, O pony . . . "I take you a riding . . ."

Children can add verses about their own pets.

Fuzzy Wuzzy

LILLIAN SCHULZ VANADA

Adapted from Traditional Russian

♩ = 1 beat. Moderately.

Fuz - zy wuz - zy, creep - y crawl - y Cat - er - pil - lar fun - ny, ___

You will be a but - ter - fly ___ when the days are sun - ny. ___

Wing - ing, fling - ing, danc - ing, spring - ing But - ter - fly so yel - low, ___

You were once a cat - er - pil - lar, Wig - gly, wig - gly fel - low. ___

Words used by permission of the author and the Association for Childhood Education
International.

Children will have fun crawling like caterpillars, flying like butterflies, or imitat-
ing these creatures in finger plays.

The Woodpecker

AGNES SANFORD

NORMAN AND MARGARET MEALY

Bird on the fir tree, Thump, thump, Bird on the fir tree, Thump.

Bird on the fir tree Peck - e - ty, peck - e - ty, Bird on the fir tree, Thump.

How do you know to go Peck - e - ty, peck - e - ty? Who ev - er told you to Thump?

Catch- ing your din-ner by Peck - e - ty, peck - e - ty, Find- ing your sup- per by Thump?

Words from *Let's Believe* by Agnes Sanford. Copyright © Harper & Brothers 1954.

Let children experiment on how to make good "thump" and "peck" noises. For instance, with rhythm sticks, by hitting two blocks together, or by drumming their fingers on the table.

Who Has Seen the Wind?

CHRISTINA ROSSETTI

Zion's Harp

𝅗𝅥 = 1 beat. Thoughtfully.

1. Who has seen the wind? _____ Nei - ther I nor __ you:
2. Who has seen the wind? _____ Nei - ther you nor __ I:

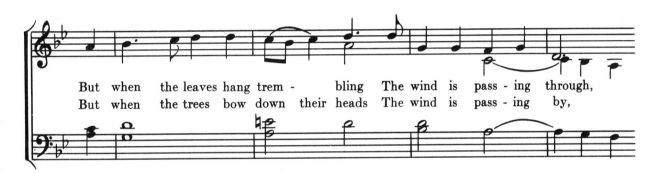

But when the leaves hang trem - bling The wind is pass - ing through,
But when the trees bow down their heads The wind is pass - ing by,

The wind is pass - ing __ through.
The wind is pass - ing __ by.

Use only the second stanza with smaller children, or let them sing the melody on "oo" to suggest the wind. A few children can be "trees," others, running by on tiptoe or without shoes, can be the "wind."

Funny

94

K P

AILEEN FISHER

PETER HALLOCK

Here is one way to teach this five-note melody. Let the children learn first the opening and closing refrain, "When you stop...." Then different children can learn the four separate phrases that make up the rest of the song. The melody can be used without accompaniment, with just the melody played in octaves (use the octave above the melody), or with the added fun of Mr. Hallock's accompaniment.

the diff - 'rence in days that are rain - y or sun - ny,

the way that our legs can be walk - y or run - ny —

slower When you stop to think of it, *fast* is - n't it fun - ny?

95 Where Do the Stars Go?

K P

ANNETTE PENNIMAN

Traditional American

♩ = 1 beat. Moderately

F   C7   F   C7   F   C7

1. Where do the stars go ___ in the day... Why is a rain - drop wet...
2. Where does the wind go ___ when it blows... Why is a ba - by small...
3. Where is to - mor-row when ___ it's to - day Why does a need - le sew...

Bb   F   G min.   F   C7   F

What makes a wheel go round ___ and ___ round... When is a dog a pet?
What makes my feet skip round ___ a - bout... When does a child grow tall?
What makes my ball bounce up ___ and ___ down... I simp - ly have to know.

Melody, "Soldier, soldier, won't you marry me," collected by Cecil J. Sharp, slightly altered
and used by permission of Novello & Co., Ltd. Copyright 1921. Copyright renewed 1949.

Weather and Seasons

96 On a Rainy Day

N K

JOSEPHINE ROYLE

JOHN P. SACCO

♩ = 1 beat. Not too fast.

G   D7

1. Rain, rain, fall - ing all a - round, Rain, rain, fall - ing on the ground;
2. One, two, now we turn a - round, Three, four, stamp up - on the ground;

G   C   G   D7   G

Who knows a game to play On a ve - ry rain - y day?
We know a game to play On a ve - ry rain - y day.

From *Listen and Sing* of "The World of Music" series. Used by permission of Ginn and
Company, owner of the copyright.

An action song adaptable also to "snow" or "sun . . . shining all around."

Rain Is Falling Down

SATIS N. COLEMAN and ALICE G. THORN   SATIS N. COLEMAN and ALICE G. THORN

This song should usually be sung unaccompanied. The children can "pitter, patter" by patting fingers of one hand on the palm of the other, or by tapping on the window as they watch the rain. The accompaniment is for rhythmic activity when the children are running on tiptoe being "raindrops." The words can be changed to: "Snow is falling down . . . softly, softly. . . ."

Rain is fall-ing down, rain is fall-ing down,

pit - ter, pat - ter, pit - ter, pat - ter, rain is fall - ing down.

From *Singing Time*, published by The John Day Company. Copyright 1929 by Satis N. Coleman and Alice G. Thorn.

98 Dance, Leaves

N K

LOUISE ABNEY

Traditional English

♩ = 1 beat. Lightly.

Au-tumn leaves are danc-ing down, are danc-ing down, are danc-ing down —

Leaves of crim-son, gold and brown Dance, leaves, dance!

Let the wind __ whirl you round, __ Make a car-pet for the ground,

Soon you'll sleep with-out a sound — Sleep, leaves, sleep!

Words, originally called "Dance of the Leaves," from *Choral Speaking Arrangements for the Lower Grades* by Abney and Rowe; reprinted by permission of Expression Company, Publishers. Combination of melody and words reprinted by permission of Edith Lovell Thomas and Beacon Press.

While children are learning this song, omit the accompaniment and play only the melody with its upper octave. The accompaniment is especially good for rhythmic activity when the children are "being leaves" rather than singing.

God of the Small Things

MARION JAMES

coll. CECIL J. SHARP

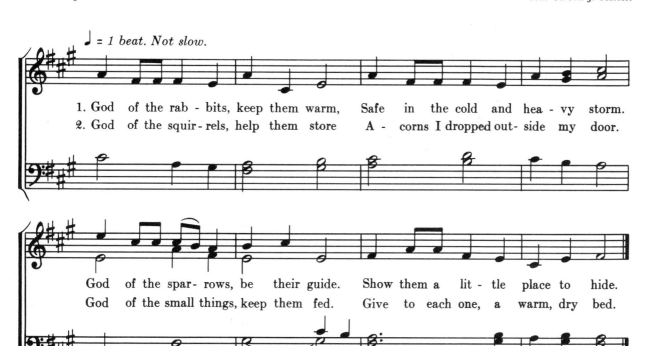

♩ = 1 beat. Not slow.

1. God of the rab - bits, keep them warm, Safe in the cold and hea - vy storm.
2. God of the squir - rels, help them store A - corns I dropped out - side my door.

God of the spar - rows, be their guide. Show them a lit - tle place to hide.
God of the small things, keep them fed. Give to each one, a warm, dry bed.

Words reprinted by permission of the Board of Parish Education of the Augustana Lutheran
Church. Melody, "The Bird Song," collected by Cecil J. Sharp and used by permission of
Novello & Co., Ltd. Copyright 1921. Copyright renewed 1949.

Mitten Song

MARIE LOUISE ALLEN

SUE HANLIN

♩ = 1 beat. Briskly.

1. "Thumbs in the thumb - place, Fin - gers all to - ge - ther!"
2. When it is cold, It does - n't mat - ter whe - ther
3. This is the song We sing in mit - ten- wea - ther:

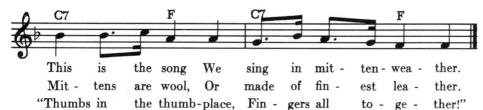

This is the song We sing in mit - ten- wea - ther.
Mit - tens are wool, Or made of fin - est lea - ther.
"Thumbs in the thumb-place, Fin - gers all to - ge - ther!"

Words from *A Pocketful of Rhymes* by Marie Louise Allen. Copyright, 1939 by Harper &
Brothers. Melody from *The First Grade Book* of "Our Singing World" series. Used by permission
of Ginn and Company, owner of the copyright.

101
KP

Winter Coats

DOROTHY ALDIS

PETER HALLOCK

♩ = 1 beat. As though telling a story.

In Oc - to - ber, when they know That ve - ry soon there will be snow,

Cows and hor - ses, sheep and goats Start to grow their win - ter coats.

Each year they grow them, fine and new (And fit - ting ver - y nice - ly too),

But with no but-tons to un-do, Nor poc-kets for a hand-ker-chief. And

so they have to snort and sniff.

Without a Sound at All

GRACE M. HAYNES

HENRY M. HALVORSON

♩.= 1 beat. With wonder.

With-out a sound at all,_____ As soft-ly as can be _____

The snow-flakes start to fall Up-on the earth and me._____

The children's fingers can be "falling snowflakes" while they sing.

103

P

When the Wheat Is Planted

Anonymous

K. G. FINLAY

♩ = 1 beat. Moderately.

1. When the wheat is plant - ed In the deep dark bed,
2. God sends sun and show - ers, Birds sing o - ver - head,
3. When the wheat is gath - ered, Stored in barn and shed,

Mo - thers pray their chil - dren Will have dai - - ly bread.
While the wheat is grow - ing For our dai - - ly bread.
Then we all are thank - ful For our dai - - ly bread.

Melody, "Glenfinlas," and harmonization used by permission of the composer.

The notes in brackets may be omitted.

104

KP

The Seed

AILEEN FISHER

NORMAN AND MARGARET MEALY

♩ = 1 beat. With movement.

How does it know, this lit - tle seed, if it is to grow to a flower or weed,

if it is to be a vine or shoot, or grow to a tree with a long deep root? A

seed is so small where do you sup - pose it stores up all of the things it knows?

Look! Look!
Our Seeds We're Planting

Anonymous

D. W.

♩ = *1 beat. Not too fast.*

1. Look!   Look!   our seeds we're plant-ing   In   a   row.
2. Look!   Look!   the sun is   shin- ing Warm and   bright.
3. Look!   Look!   the plants are grow- ing. First they're small.

Soft - ly,   soft - ly,   cov - er them.___ Will   they grow?
Look!___   Look! the   rain is   fall - ing Soft   and   light.
Up! ___   Up! ___   see them stand-ing Straight and   tall.

Words reprinted by permission of Edith Lovell Thomas and Beacon Press.

Use finger plays with this song, or let the children be "seeds"

that "grow."

For a hymn about planting in *The Hymnal 1940*, see:
    138   "We plow the fields, and scatter" (stanza 1)   P

Morning at the Beach

JOHN FARRAR

NORMAN AND MARGARET MEALY

♩ = 1 beat. Brightly.

1. There's soap- suds on the waves, There's white foam in the sky,
2. There are fish- es in the sea, How ma- ny do you think?

The peb- bles on the beach are wet, And so am I.
How ma- ny shin- ing fish- es And do they drink?

3. If fish- es do drink wa- ter — Some day, per- haps, they'll try

To drink and drink and drink *and drink* The o - cean *dry!*

Words of "Morning at the Beach" by John Farrar. Copyright © 1930 by Richard R. Smith, Inc.

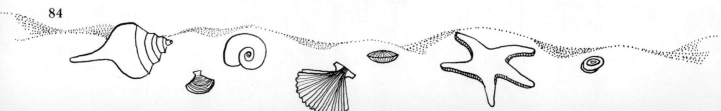

A Good Day

MARION JAMES   Traditional English

The farm is spill - ing o - ver With bu - sy things to - day.
The lambs are act - ing diz - zy And jump - ing to and fro.

Fine

The farm - er's cut - ting clo - ver To fill the barn with hay. ___
The farm is fun ___ and bu - sy, For God has made it so! ___

The air is sweet and sun - ny. The grass is sweet and warm. ___

D.C. al Fine

The bees are mak - ing hon - ey And buzz - ing near the swarm. ___

Words reprinted by permission of the Board of Parish Education of the Augustana Lutheran Church.

108

NKP

Thanks for Meadows

BERTHA WILCOX SMITH

Cantiques à l'Usage des Ecoles du Dimanche

Words used by permission of the author; first published in *Highlights for Children.*

For other songs to God as Creator or about the wonders of His created world, see:

32	This Is the Day	P
50	Sing to Our God	P
52	Gloria, Gloria	K P
61	Benedicite	P
68	All Good Gifts Around Us	N K P
70	A Thank You Prayer	P
71	We Thank Thee, God, for Hands to Feel	K P
72	For Little Things	N K
75	Some Things We Are Specially Glad About	N K P
109	God Shines in Every Star	K P
114	They Blaze a Pathway to the Moon	P
121	The Sun	N K
125	Trust in God, Our Maker	P
147	To an Airplane	P

For a list of hymns about God the Creator in *The Hymnal 1940,* see page 133.

Within God's world we sing—
With joy, with wonder, with penitent hearts.
And of His world we sing—
Of family and friends, and things around us.

God Cares for You and Me

GOD CARES FOR EVERYONE

GOD CARES FOR ME

GOD CARES FOR MY FAMILY

GOD CARES FOR MY FRIENDS AND NEIGHBORS

GOD CARES FOR US IN WORK AND PLAY

109

KP

God Shines in Every Star

VICTORIA SAFFELLE JOHNSON

LEIGHTON G. HAYNE

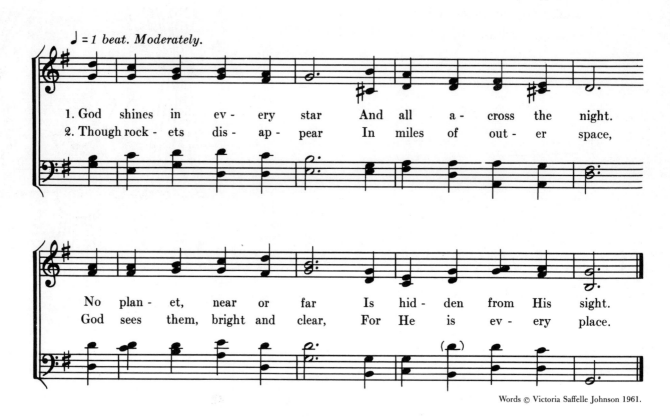

♩ = 1 beat. Moderately.

1. God shines in ev - ery star And all a - cross the night.
2. Though rock - ets dis - ap - pear In miles of out - er space,

No plan - et, near or far Is hid - den from His sight.
God sees them, bright and clear, For He is ev - ery place.

This melody, "St. Cecilia," appears in *The Hymnal 1940* at #544.

Thou Art with Us

FLORENCE M. TAYLOR   CHRISTIAN FRIEDRICH WITT, alt.

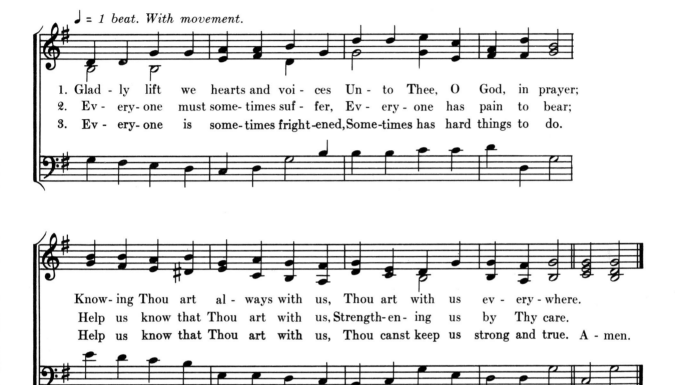

♩ = 1 beat. With movement.

1. Glad - ly lift we hearts and voi - ces Un - to Thee, O God, in prayer;
2. Ev - ery-one must some-times suf - fer, Ev - ery-one has pain to bear;
3. Ev - ery-one is some-times fright-ened, Some-times has hard things to do.

Know- ing Thou art al - ways with us, Thou art with us ev - ery - where.
Help us know that Thou art with us, Strength-en - ing us by Thy care.
Help us know that Thou art with us, Thou canst keep us strong and true. A - men.

Words from *Children's Religion*, August 1941. Copyright, The Pilgrim Press. Used by permission.

This melody, "Stuttgart," appears in *The Hymnal 1940* at #1, #48, and #280.

111
P

God's Children Speak in Different Tongues

NANCY BYRD TURNER

Traditional English

♩ = 1 beat. With movement.

God's — chil - dren speak in dif - ferent tongues, With — dif - ferent things — to say,

And — dif - ferent tasks and dif - ferent toys, And — ma -ny a dif - ferent way;

And — some are dark, — and some are fair, And — some are — scarce - ly known;

But — each is kin — to — all the rest, And — each the Fa - ther's own.

This is the second stanza of a longer poem. Words from *Song and Play for Children,* by Danielson and Conant. Copyright, The Pilgrim Press. Used by permission. Melody, "Kingsfold," taken from *Songs of Praise* (Enlarged Edition) by permission of the Oxford University Press, London, England.

This melody appears in *The Hymnal 1940* at #101 and #331.

It Makes No Difference, East or West

112

P

ETHEL WENDELL TROUT

Alt. from *Southern Harmony*

♩ = 1 beat. With breadth.

1. It makes no dif - ference, East or West, Wher - ev - er we may be,
2. It makes no dif - ference, North or South, Wher - ev - er we may be,

God is our Fa - ther, Friend, and Guide, His gifts are showered on ev - ery side;
God loves His chil - dren ev - ery - where, And guards us with His ten - der care;

He cares for you and me.
He loves both you and me.

Words from *Hymns for Junior Worship*. Copyright, 1927, renewed, 1955, by the Presbyterian Board of Christian Education. Used by permission.

Note the rhythmic interest created by the two beats in measure 3.

The Gospel Tells What God Has Done

113

P

CAROL CHRISTOPHER DRAKE

Music as above

The Gospel tells what God has done
For love of you and me.
To win our love He lived with us
And taught us love by giving first
The best there is, Himself.

114 They Blaze a Pathway to the Moon

P

VICTORIA SAFFELLE JOHNSON   WIRTEMBERG

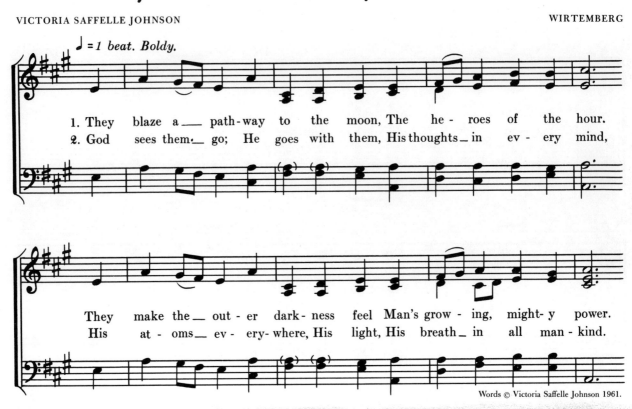

♩ = 1 beat. Boldy.

1. They blaze a ___ path-way to the moon, The he - roes of the hour.
2. God sees them ___ go; He goes with them, His thoughts ___ in ev - ery mind,

They make the ___ out - er dark - ness feel Man's grow - ing, might- y power.
His at - oms ___ ev - ery-where, His light, His breath ___ in all man - kind.

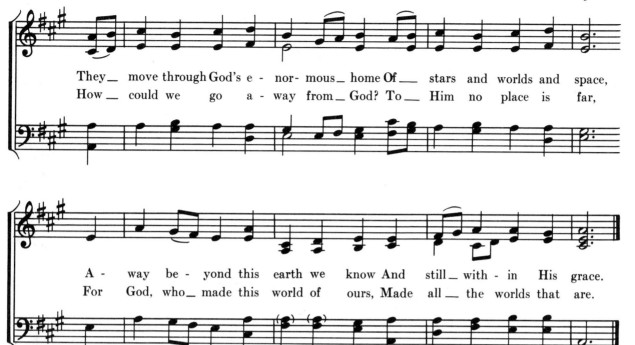

They__ move through God's e - nor- mous__ home Of__ stars and worlds and space,
How__ could we go a - way from__ God? To__ Him no place is far,

A - way be - yond this earth we know And still__ with - in His grace.
For God, who__ made this world of ours, Made all__ the worlds that are.

This melody, "Ellacombe," appears in *The Hymnal 1940* at #96 and #187.

Prayer for Sick Children

115

P

LADY EDITH FLORENCE BOYLE MACALISTER, alt.

Nürnberg *Gesangbuch*

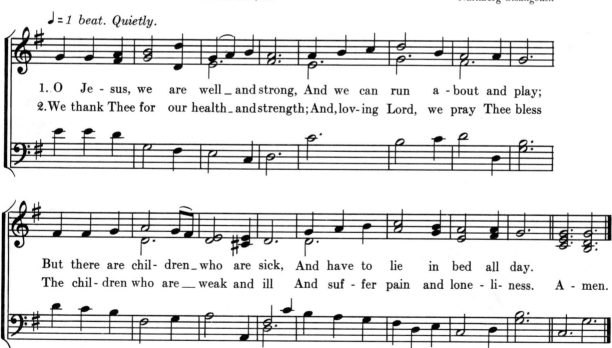

♩ = 1 beat. Quietly.

1. O Je - sus, we are well__ and strong, And we can run a - bout and play;
2. We thank Thee for our health__ and strength; And, lov-ing Lord, we pray Thee bless

But there are chil- dren__ who are sick, And have to lie in bed all day.
The chil - dren who are__ weak and ill And suf - fer pain and lone - li - ness. A - men.

This song can help children express a concern for their friends who are sick at home or in hospitals.

116

K

Bless These Gifts

LOUISE M. OGLEVEE, alt.

LEE H. BRISTOL, JR.

♩ = 1 beat. Moderately.

Bless these gifts, our Fa - ther, As we try to __ share

With your ma - ny chil - dren, Here and ev - 'ry - where. A - men.

Music reprinted by permission of Lee H. Bristol, Jr.

117

K P

Father, Bless Our Gifts

ANNE KENDRICK BENEDICT, alt.

FELIX MENDELSSOHN, melody

♩ = 1 beat. Thoughtfully.

1. Fa - ther, bless our gifts, we __ pray Thee, As they tra - vel on their way;
2. Fa - ther, there are chil - dren __ liv - ing With - out food or homes or care;

May they car - ry joy to __ ma - ny Who are __ sick and can - not play.
We would help them by our __ giv - ing: Hear, dear __ Lord, this sim - ple prayer. A - men.

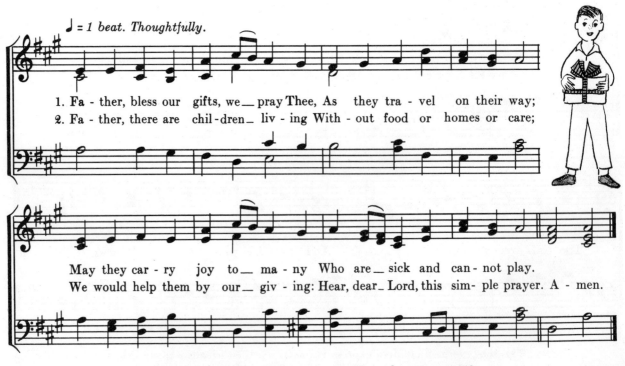

94

This melody, "Trust," appears in *The Hymnal 1940* at #448.

Father, Bless the Gifts We Bring Thee

Unknown

Traditional English

Fa - ther, bless the gifts we bring Thee, Give them some-thing good to do;

May they help some-one to love Thee; Fa - ther, may we love Thee too. A - men.

Melody, "Sussex," taken from *Songs of Praise* (Enlarged Edition) by permission of the Oxford University Press, London, England.

Closing Prayer

119

K P

NORMAN B. QUIGG

WILLIAM JONES

Dear Fa - ther, bless each — child of Thine And — keep us — all, we / pray,

Safe in Thy lov - ing care Un - til we come an - oth - er day. A - men.

This melody, "St. Stephen," appears in *The Hymnal 1940* at #11 and #249.

For All God's Children

120

JESSIE ELEANOR MOORE

Cantiques à l'Usage des Ecoles du Dimanche

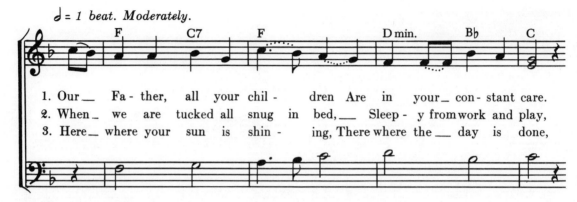

1. Our __ Fa - ther, all your chil - dren Are in your __ con - stant care.
2. When __ we are tucked all snug in bed, __ Sleep - y from work and play,
3. Here __ where your sun is shin - ing, There where the __ day is done,

Teach us to love each oth - er, Help us to learn __ to __ share.
The day is just be - gin - ning For chil - dren far a - way.
Yel - low, or brown, or black, or white, __ Bless us ev - ery __ one. A - men.

Words from *Children's Prayers for Everyday* by Jessie Eleanor Moore; copyright © 1949 by Pierce and Smith. Used by permission of Abingdon Press, Publishers.

For other songs about God's care and love for everyone, see:

For a list of appropriate hymns in *The Hymnal 1940*, see page 133.

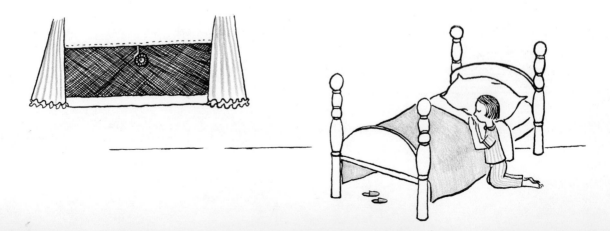

The Sun

HELEN WRIGHT SALISBURY   NORMAN AND MARGARET MEALY

When the sun wakes up in the morn-ing, It wakes me right up too,___

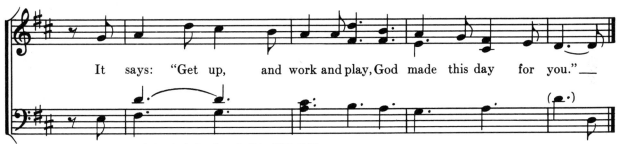

It says: "Get up, and work and play, God made this day for you."___

Words from *Finger Fun: Songs and Rhythms for the Very Young*, by Helen Wright Salisbury,
published by Cowman Publications, Inc.

Good Morning, God, Now It Is Light

A Church School Class   NORMAN AND MARGARET MEALY

Good morn - ing, God, Now it is light

Thank You for keep - ing me Safe through the night.

Words from "Prayers for Boys and Girls," compiled by the Department of Christian
Education of the Protestant Episcopal Church.

By substituting "us" for "me," a family could use this at its morning prayer.

123
How Strong and Sure My Father's Care

K P

Anonymous

THOMAS TALLIS

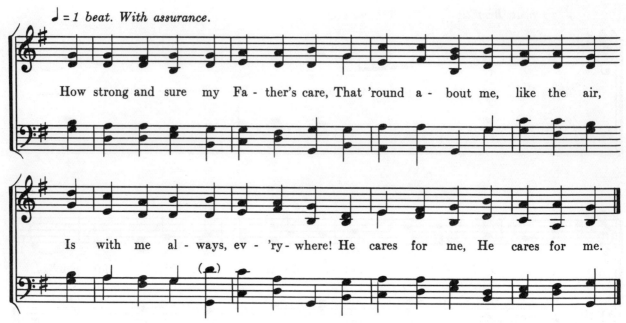

♩ = *1 beat. With assurance.*

How strong and sure my Fa - ther's care, That 'round a - bout me, like the air,

Is with me al - ways, ev - 'ry - where! He cares for me, He cares for me.

Two groups of children can sing this as a canon. The second group begins the song when the first has reached "my." If you use the accompaniment, repeat the last four chords.

This melody, "Tallis' Canon," appears in *The Hymnal 1940* at #165.

124
Heavenly Father, Hear My Prayer

P

Anonymous

Traditional Welsh

♩ = *1 beat. Moderately.*

Heav'n - ly Fa - ther,_ hear my prayer. Day and night I'm in _ Thy _ care.

Bless my _ friends and fam - i - ly; Let my _ home have room for Thee;

98

Bless all those _ with _ whom I play; Help us love Thee ev - ery _ day. A - men.

This hymn may be made more useful for classes and families by changing the "I" and "my" to "we" and "our."

Trust in God, Our Maker

125

P

GEORGE WALLACE BRIGGS   THOMAS TALLIS

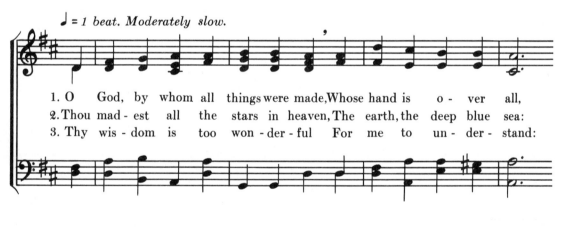

♩ = 1 beat. Moderately slow.

1. O God, by whom all things were made, Whose hand is o - ver all,
2. Thou mad - est all the stars in heaven, The earth, the deep blue sea:
3. Thy wis - dom is too won - der - ful For me to un - der - stand:

Be - yond Thy care can no man stray, Nor can a spar - row fall.
Thou mad - est man to know Thy love; And so Thou mad - est me.
But this I know, in this I trust, That I am in Thy hand. A - men.

This melody, "Tallis' Ordinal," appears in *The Hymnal 1940* at #298 and #382.

Growing Up

MARCHETTE CHUTE   WILLIAM BOHN

♩ = 1 beat. Deliberately.

mf

When I grow up I'll car-ry a stick And be ve-ry dig-ni-fied;

I'll have a watch that will real-ly tick, My house will be tall and built of brick,

retarding   *joyfully first tempo*

And no one will guess that it's just a trick And I'm real-ly my-self in-side.

Words reprinted from *St Nicholas Magazine*.

Ask one or two children to act this out while the others sing.

My Secret Place

GWENDOLYN BROOKS   NORMAN AND MARGARET MEALY

I have a se-cret place to go. Not a-ny-one may know.

And some-times when the wind is rough I can-not get there fast e-nough.

And some-times when my mo - ther Is scold-ing my big bro - ther,

My se-cret place, it seems to me, Is quite the on-ly place to be.

Words from *Bronzeville Boys and Girls* (original title, "Keziah"), by Gwendolyn Brooks, published by Harpers & Brothers. Copyright © 1956 by Gwendolyn Brooks Blakely.

This is a whimsical song to be sung to children for fun. Use it to show a child
you know how he sometimes feels.

128 I Can Help

Verses 1 and 2: MARGARET L. CRAIN   MARGARET SAWIN

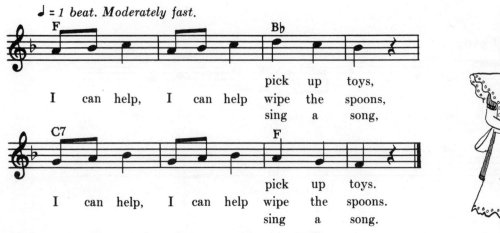

♩ = 1 beat. Moderately fast.

I can help, I can help
pick up toys,
wipe the spoons,
sing a song,

I can help, I can help
pick up toys.
wipe the spoons.
sing a song.

Verses 1 and 2 and melody from *Nursery Songs and Rhythms* compiled by Margaret L. Crain.
Copyright, 1953. The Judson Press. Used by permission.

Many variations are possible: "Would you help," "John can help," "Who can help," etc.

129 Then

DOROTHY ALDIS   D. W.

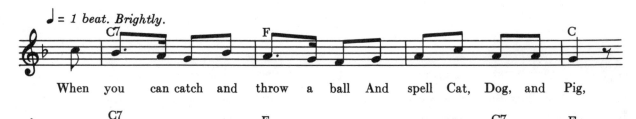

♩ = 1 beat. Brightly.

When you can catch and throw a ball And spell Cat, Dog, and Pig,

Then you have fin - ished be - ing small And start - ed be - ing Big.

Words from *Hop! Skip! and Jump!* by Dorothy Aldis. Copyright 1934 by Dorothy Aldis.
Published by Minton-Balch Co. Used by the permission of G. P. Putnam's Sons.

   For a list of hymns about "Me" in *The Hymnal 1940*, see page 134.

Counting Song

MAY JUSTUS

ZILPHIA HORTON

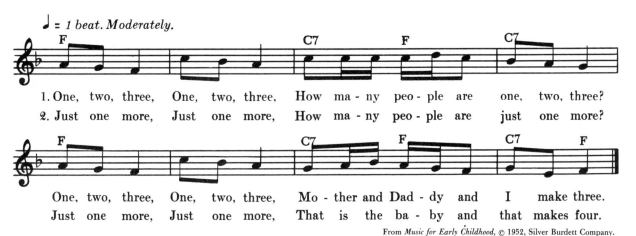

1. One, two, three, One, two, three, How ma-ny peo-ple are one, two, three?
2. Just one more, Just one more, How ma-ny peo-ple are just one more?

One, two, three, One, two, three, Mo-ther and Dad-dy and I make three.
Just one more, Just one more, That is the ba-by and that makes four.

From *Music for Early Childhood,* © 1952, Silver Burdett Company.

At home, use names of particular children instead of "I" and "baby" ("Mother and Daddy and Mark make three"; "That is David and he makes four"). In class, substitute children's names throughout ("Tommy and Johnny and Susan make three"; "That is Becky and she makes four").

A Friendly House

JESSIE ELEANOR MOORE

Adapted from the traditional Haitian

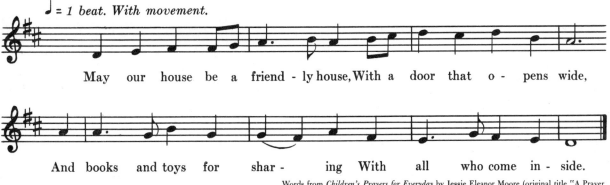

May our house be a friend-ly house, With a door that o-pens wide,

And books and toys for shar-ing With all who come in-side.

Words from *Children's Prayers for Everyday* by Jessie Eleanor Moore (original title "A Prayer for Guests"); copyright © 1949 by Pierce and Smith. Used by permission of Abingdon Press, Publishers.

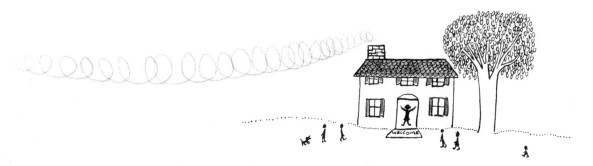

Alone We Could Not Learn to Read

132

P

CAROL CHRISTOPHER DRAKE

The Union Harmony

♩ = 1 beat. Not too slow.

A - lone we could not __ learn to __ read, At school they teach us how;

Nor __ could we __ learn to trust un - less Our fam - i - lies taught __ us how.

We __ love be - cause God loved us __ first And lov - ing shows __ us how.

This melody, "Morning Song," appears in *The Hymnal 1940* at #156 and #494.

Parents

GWENDOLYN BROOKS

Traditional American

I had a dream last night. I dreamed I had to pick a Mo-ther out.
I had to choose a Fa-ther too. At first, I won-dered what to do,

There were so ma-ny__ there, it seemed, Short and tall and thin and stout.

But just be-fore I sprang a-wake, I knew what par-ents I would take.

And *this* sur-prised and__ made me glad: They were the ones I al-ways had!

Words from *Bronzeville Boys and Girls* (original title, "Andre") by Gwendolyn Brooks,
published by Harper & Brothers. Copyright © 1956 by Gwendolyn Brooks Blakely. Melody,
"Sweet William" (slightly altered), taken from *English Folk Songs from the Southern
Appalachians* by permission of the Oxford University Press, London, England.

Like #127, this is a whimsical song. Sing it for fun—or to show a child that you know how he sometimes feels.

134

NK

Lullaby

THERESA C. LORBIECKI   Traditional English

1. Mo - ther Ma - ry rocked her Child, As I now rock __ you.
2. Mo - ther Ma - ry rocked her Child. Lit - tle Je - sus __ knew

Soon He closed His lit - tle eyes And to dreams He __ flew.
That she rocked Him lov - ing - ly, As I now rock __ you.

Melody "Devonshire" (slightly altered), taken from *Songs of Praise* (Enlarged Edition) by permission of the Oxford University Press, London, England.

This is a song for a mother or father to sing to a child at bedtime, for a teacher to use in leading a bit of play-acting, or for a child to sing to her doll.

135

N

Baby Dear

Traditional American   Traditional American

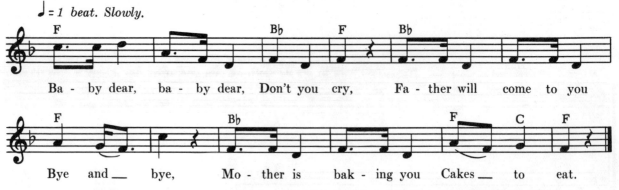

Ba - by dear, ba - by dear, Don't you cry, Fa - ther will come to you

Bye and __ bye, Mo - ther is bak - ing you Cakes __ to eat.

From *American Folk Songs for Children* by Ruth Crawford Seeger, published by Doubleday & Company; reprinted by permission of Charles Seeger.

Use a child's name in place of "Baby dear" if you wish. Substitute names of friends and relatives in place of "Father" and "Mother" for additional verses. Children can sing the song to a baby brother or sister—or to a favorite doll.

Sleepy Song

MARION JAMES

Traditional English

♩ = 1 beat. *Quietly.*

1. Close your eyes and go to sleep. God and lov - ing an - gels keep
2. Calves are qui - et in the hay Where they've frol - icked through the day.

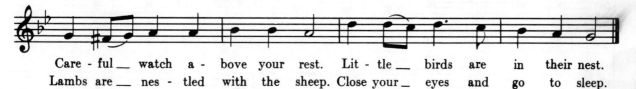

Care - ful watch a - bove your rest. Lit - tle birds are in their nest.
Lambs are nes - tled with the sheep. Close your eyes and go to sleep.

Words reprinted by permission of the Board of Parish Education of the Augustana Lutheran Church.

Parents can sing this to their children at bedtime.

Cooperation

JESSIE ELEANOR MOORE

D.W.

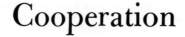

♩ = 1 beat. *Moderately.*

1. Mo - ther cooks the din - ner For Dad - dy and for me,
2. Dad - dy's been at work all day For Mo - ther and for me.

And I set the tab - le For all of us three.
Thank you, God, for love and care In our fam - i - ly.

Words from *Children's Prayers for Everyday* by Jessie Eleanor Moore: copyright © 1949 by
Pierce and Smith. Used by permission of Abingdon Press, Publishers.

138

KP

I Had a Feeling

DOROTHY ALDIS   PETER HALLOCK

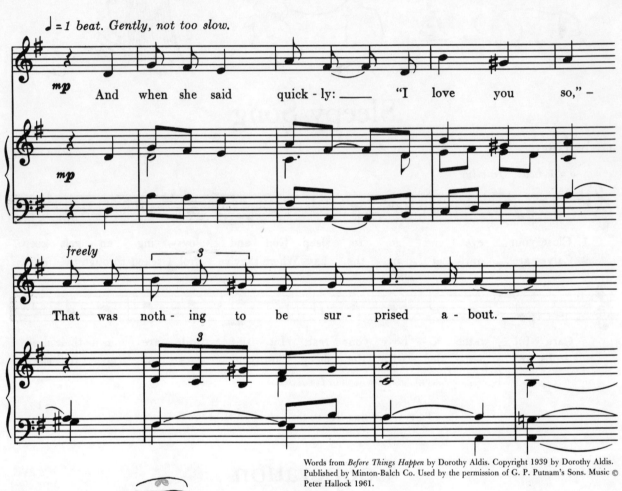

♩ = 1 beat. Gently, not too slow.

mp And when she said quick-ly: ___ "I love you so," —

freely

That was noth-ing to be sur-prised a-bout. ___

Words from *Before Things Happen* by Dorothy Aldis. Copyright 1939 by Dorothy Aldis.
Published by Minton-Balch Co. Used by the permission of G. P. Putnam's Sons. Music ©
Peter Hallock 1961.

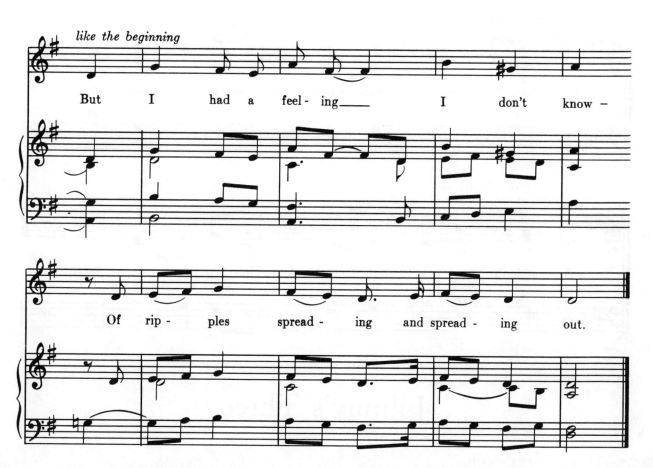

like the beginning

But I had a feel-ing___ I don't know —

Of rip - ples spread - ing and spread - ing out.

Teachers can sing this song to boys and girls after talk about mothers and the love that is shown in family life. Later the youngsters may learn to sing it themselves. The melody can be sung without accompaniment.

139
NKP

Birthday Song

WILLIAM B. SCHMIDGALL

WILLIAM B. SCHMIDGALL

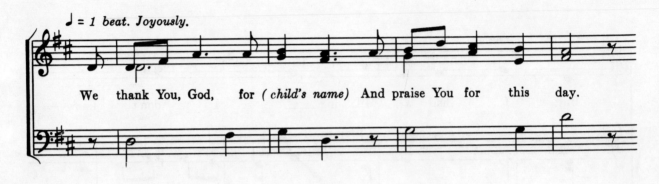

We thank You, God, for *(child's name)* And praise You for this day.

Be with us in our fam-i-ly, And bless him now, we pray.
(her)

"Family" can mean "church family" as well as those at home.

140
NK

Johnny's Three

Stanza 1: MARGARET L. CRAIN
Stanza 2: NORMAN AND MARGARET MEALY

MARGARET L. CRAIN

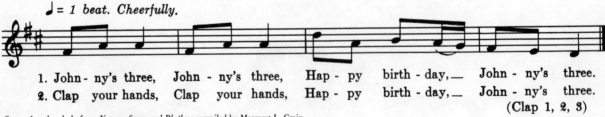

1. John-ny's three, John-ny's three, Hap-py birth-day,— John-ny's three.
2. Clap your hands, Clap your hands, Hap-py birth-day,— John-ny's three.
(Clap 1, 2, 3)

Stanza 1 and melody from *Nursery Songs and Rhythms* compiled by Margaret L. Crain.
Copyright, 1953. The Judson Press. Used by permission.

You can substitute any name and any age.

For other songs about "My Family," see:
24   Dear Lord Jesus   P
124   Heavenly Father, Hear My Prayer   P

For a list of hymns about "My Family" in *The Hymnal 1940*, see page 134.

Love One Another

EDITH SLOANE   EDITH SLOANE

♩ = 1 beat. Moderately slow.

"Love one an-oth - er," "Love one an-oth - er,"

"Love one an-oth - er," Je - sus said.

This song can be sung as a round. For directions, see page 129.

New Year's Song

Traditional English   D.W.

♩ = 1 beat. Cheerfully.

God _ bless you all, both great and small,

And send you a hap - py New Year!

Community Helpers

Stanza 1: ELIZABETH GRENOBLE
Stanza 2: NORMAN AND MARGARET MEALY
ELIZABETH GRENOBLE

♩ = 1 beat. Moderately.

1. I am a man who works like this, I help you all I can;
2. My dad - dy works and works like this, He helps us all he can;

I work like this, I work like this, Can you guess who I am?
He works like this, he works like this, He is a (teach - er).
(mail - man), etc.

Stanza 1 and melody from *Music for Early Childhood*, © 1952, Silver Burdett Company.

Children can take turns "being" various community helpers.

111

Here's the Proud Policeman

144

KP

PHYLLIS McGINLEY

WILLIAM BOHN

Here is one way to teach this song. After you have sung it to the children a few times, have them sing the opening sentence with you. Next, have them join in at "By daylight he protects you; He protects you through the dark," or "When you want to cross the street." Add a phrase or two at a time until the entire song is familiar.

Here's the proud Po-lice-man With but-tons po-lished neat.

He's pleased to put his hand up When you want to cross the street.

By day-light he pro-tects you; He pro-tects you through the dark,

And he points the way po-lite-ly To the play-ground or the park.

Playing Fireman

145
N K

ELEANOR GRAHAM VANCE   MARION BAUER

♩ = 1 beat. With vigor.

Bong! Bong! Bong! Bong! Where's the fire? Where's the fire?

Bong! Bong! Bong! Bong! Start the truck! Start the truck!

Bong! Bong! Bong! Bong! Squirt the hose! Squirt the hose!

From *Music for Early Childhood*, © 1952, Silver Burdett Company. Music reprinted by permission of Harrison Potter.

Bong! Bong! Bong! Bong! Put the fire out! Put the fire out!

Stop the music long enough for the children to add a siren if they wish to. The song may be taught and sung without accompaniment, saving the excitement of the piano for a special treat or for a time when the youngsters are busy acting out the song.

A class can make up another song about community helpers on the model of:

    75   Some Things We Are Specially Glad About   N K P

For other songs about friends and neighbors, see:

    55   Baptized with Water   K P
  124   Heavenly Father, Hear My Prayer   P
  151   We're Making Valentines   N K

For two hymns about friends and neighbors in *The Hymnal 1940*, see page 134.

Here's the Bus

146

KP

PHYLLIS McGINLEY, alt.

WILLIAM BOHN

♩. = 1 beat. *Brightly.*

Here's   the Bus, __   the boun - cing Bus, That bears __   a shop - per store - ward.

It's fun to sit __ In back of it But __ seats are bet - ter for - ward.

Words from *All Around the Town* by Phyllis McGinley. Copyright ©, 1948, by Phyllis
McGinley. Published by J. P. Lippincott Company. Reprinted by permission of the author.

116

Al - though it's big   as buil - dings are   And looks both bold and grand, ___   It

has ___ to stop o - bli - ging - ly   If you ___ but raise your hand, to stop ___

If   you   but raise ___ your hand. ___

This song offers good opportunity for dramatic play. The accompaniment is needed to provide the "bounce" for the bus.

147
P

To an Airplane

AGNES SANFORD   *Southern Harmony*

You're as hea - vy, as hea - vy, as hea - vy as lead, —
Soar - ing and roar - ing up o - ver my head —

And yet you're so light you can fly,
And high in the sum - mer - y sky!

Men made you hea - vy, — yet men made you fly

On shim - mer - ing, sil - ver - y wings,

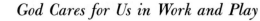

And if men can do that, then I do not see why—

They should won - der at heav - en - ly things!

Come to My House

JOHN HARRELL

JOHN HARRELL

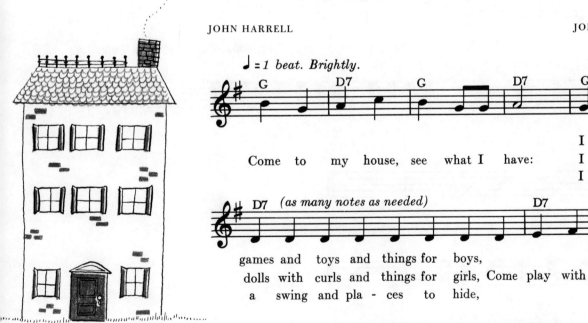

♩ = 1 beat. Brightly.

G   D7   G   D7   G

Come to my house, see what I have: I have
                                     I have
                                     I have

D7   *(as many notes as needed)*   D7   G

games and toys and things for boys,
dolls with curls and things for girls, Come play with me.
a swing and pla - ces to hide,

Each child can make up his own list to follow "I have . . ."

The Train

149

N K

ANN STERLING BOESEL

ANN STERLING BOESEL

Reprinted by permission of Charles Boesel.

Repeat the "choo choo" measures as needed to get the "train" started and to bring
it to a station. The "train" may want to start slowly and speed up.

120

Molly Wore Her Red Dress

Traditional American   Traditional American

♩ = 1 beat. With spirit.

Mol - ly wore her red dress, — red dress, — red dress, —

Mol - ly wore her red dress — All day long.

Original title, "Mary Was a Red Bird." Collected, adapted, and arranged by John A. and
Alan Lomax. Copyright 1941 by John A. Lomax in the book *Our Singing Country*. Copyright
assigned 1957 to Ludlow Music, Inc., New York, N.Y. Used by permission.

Sing about each child in the family or class. Substitute his name and something
he is wearing—"Indian belt," "new brown shoes," etc.

We're Making Valentines

D.W.   D.W.

♩. = 1 beat. Moderately.

We're mak - ing Val - en - tines, ____ We're mak - ing Val - en - tines, ____

For dad- dys and mo-thers, and sis - ters and bro-thers, And some for spe - cial friends. _

This song can be adapted to other family and class projects: "We're making
Christmas cards. . . ," or "We're coloring Easter eggs. . . ."

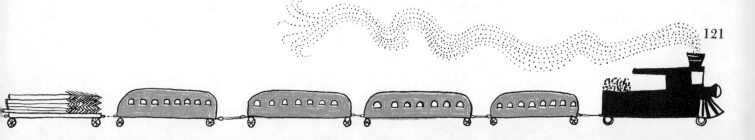

152

K

Finger Painting

GINA BAXTER

NORMAN AND MARGARET MEALY

♩. = 1 beat. Not too fast.

1. First low on the pa - per, then high, high,
2. I put in a yel - low sun quick, quick,

My goo - ey blue hand makes sea and sky. ___
The paint ___ will soon grow much too thick.

___ Swirl for a head, ___ then swish, ___ swish,
The pa - per is wet, but my pic - ture done. __

My or - ange fin - gers are paint - ing a fish.
___ Fin - ger paint - ing is won - der - ful fun.

153

N K

Put Away Song

Nursery Department of
St. Alban's Episcopal Church, Los Angeles

Traditional English

♩. = 1 beat. Briskly.

Let us put our toys a - way, Our toys a - way, our toys a - way,

Let us put our toys a - way, Safe for play ___ an - o - ther day.

Change the words for different activities: "Let us put our coats on now . . . it's
time to say good-by," "Let's join hands in a circle now . . . to play a favorite
game," etc.

Dolly's Lullaby

Anonymous

A Ten-Year-Old Child

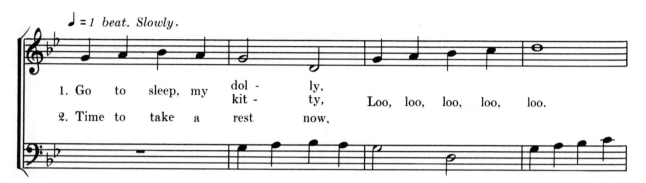

1. Go to sleep, my dol - ly,
   kit - ty,   Loo, loo, loo, loo, loo.
2. Time to take a rest now,

Close your eyes and go to sleep, While I sing to you.

Verse 1 from *Music for Early Childhood,* © 1952, Silver Burdett Company. Music from *Music and Movement,* by Ann Driver, published by the Oxford University Press, London, England.

This lullaby may be sung to dolls while children are playing house, to children themselves at rest time, or as a night song at home, using the child's name in place of "dolly."

Jim Along Josie

Traditional American   Traditional American

♩ = 1 beat. Moderately.

Hey jim a - long, ___ jim a - long Jo - sie, Hey jim a - long, ___ jim a - long Jo.

Use this for several activities: "Let's clap hands now, jim along Josie . . . ," "Let's go walking . . . ," "Stretch your arms up . . . ," "Let's sit down now. . . ."

Here are some other suggestions for rhythmic activity:

HOPPING OR JUMPING: *Crisp and lively. Somewhat slower and heavier for "Jump, jim a - long."*

Hop jim a - long, ___ jim a - long Jo - sie, Hop jim a - long, ___ jim a - long Jo.

RUNNING: *As fast as possible, lightly.*

Run (jim) a - long, ___ jim a - long Jo - sie, Run (jim) a - long, ___ jim a - long Jo.

CRAWLING: *Moderately slow, smooth.*

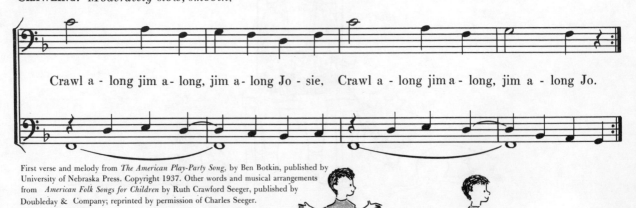

Crawl a - long jim a - long, jim a - long Jo - sie, Crawl a - long jim a - long, jim a - long Jo.

First verse and melody from *The American Play-Party Song*, by Ben Botkin, published by University of Nebraska Press. Copyright 1937. Other words and musical arrangements from *American Folk Songs for Children* by Ruth Crawford Seeger, published by Doubleday & Company; reprinted by permission of Charles Seeger.

Little Hands

Unknown

NORMAN AND MARGARET MEALY

♩ = 1 beat. Moderately.

1. Op - en, shut them; op - en, shut them; Give a lit - tle clap;
2. Creep them, creep them slow - ly up - ward Past your chin and cheek;

Op - en, shut them; op - en, shut them; Lay them in your lap.
Op - en wide your shin - ing eyes and Through your fin - gers peek.

Words (alt.) from *Finger Plays and How to Use Them*, edited by Tessa Colina; © Standard Publishing 1952.

Sandy Maloney

Traditional English

Traditional English

♩.= 1 beat. Brightly.

1. Can you dance San - dy Ma - lon - ey? Can you dance San - dy Ma - lon - ey?
2. Put both your hands on your shoul - ders, Put both your hands on your shoul - ders,
3. Here we dance San - dy Ma - lon - ey, Here we dance San - dy Ma - lon - ey,

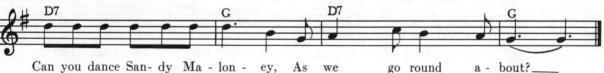

Can you dance San - dy Ma - lon - ey, As we go round a - bout?____
Put both your hands on your shoul - ders, And turn you round a - bout.____
Here we dance San - dy Ma - lon - ey, As we go round a - bout.____

4. Put out your hands before you (3 times)
   And turn you round about.
5. Same as verse 3.
6. Put both your hands in your pockets (3 times)
   And turn you round about.
7. Same as verse 3.

The group skips in a circle for verses 1, 3, 5, 7. On the other verses the group stops and does what the words say. The game can also be played with one child in the center leading off verse 2 with a different suggestion of where to "Put both your hands." While the group skips in verse 3, the center child chooses someone to take his place.

158
NK

The Doggy Game

Words and music by a Group of Children

♩ = 1 beat. Cheerfully.

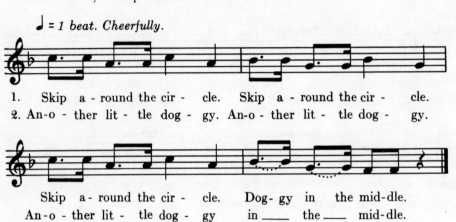

1. Skip a-round the cir - cle. Skip a-round the cir - cle.
2. An-o - ther lit - tle dog - gy. An-o - ther lit - tle dog - gy.

Skip a-round the cir - cle. Dog-gy in the mid-dle.
An-o - ther lit - tle dog - gy in the mid-dle.

Reprinted by permission of Melmont Publishers, Inc.

The children join hands and form a circle around one child, skipping or walking as they sing. At the words, "Another little doggy," the child in the center, with eyes closed, chooses someone to take his place.

159
KP

Crocodile Song

Igorot Game Song, alt.

Traditional Igorot

♩ = 1 beat. Quickly.

Croc - o - dile, Croc - o - dile, whom else are you look - ing for?

You did not like wig - gly Eel, You love Fish and no one more.

Contributed by the teachers of All Saints' Mission Elementary School, Bontoc, Mt. Province, Philippines.

When played on land: One child acts as the crocodile and hides in an area set off as "no man's land." Entering this area, the children tease the crocodile by singing this song as they look for it. At the end of the song the crocodile comes out from its hiding place and tries to catch a victim, who becomes the new crocodile.

When played in the water: The children all stay on a rock singing the song to tease the crocodile, who is in the water. At the end of the song, the crocodile pulls all the children off the rock. When the last one is off, all, including the crocodile, climb back on the rock. The last child on the rock becomes the new crocodile.

Who Built the Ark?

Traditional American   Traditional American

♩ = 1 beat. With energy.

Refrain: Who built the ark? No - ah, No - ah,

Who built the ark? Bro - ther No - ah built the ark. *(Fine)*

1. Now didn't old ___ No - ah build the ark? ___
2. Now in come the an - i - mals two by two, ___
3. Now in come the an - i - mals three by three, ___
4. Now in come the an - i - mals four by four, ___
5. Now No - ah ___ says, go shut that door, The

(Refrain after each verse)

Built it ___ out ___ of a hick - o - ry bark. ___
Hip - po - pot - a - mus and kan - ga - roo, ___
Two big ___ cats ___ and a bum - ble bee, ___
Two through the win - dow and ___ two through the door, ___
rain's start - ed drop - ping and we can't ___ take more. ___

At first, have the children sing the answers "Noah, Noah" and "Brother Noah built the ark." Then have two groups of children question and answer each other in the refrain. Finally let individual youngsters sing separate verses, with the refrain sung by the two groups as before.

For other fun songs, see:

Words from *American Folk Songs for Children* by Ruth Crawford Seeger, published by Doubleday & Company; reprinted by permission of Charles Seeger. Melody from *Rolling Along in Song* by J. Rosamond Johnson. Copyright 1937 by The Viking Press, Inc., and reprinted with their permission. Original title, "Who Built de Ark?"

The Use of Music with Young Children

Here are some suggestions about introducing and teaching songs which may be helpful, whether you have children of your own, or whether you work with parish youngsters.

SINGING IN THE HOME...

FAMILY singing, like family praying, can be done at any time. Fathers and mothers will find songs in this book to sing with their children on all sorts of occasions, or just for fun. There are waking up songs, short hymns for family prayer, and graces for meal time. There are songs to brighten a long afternoon, and going-to-bed songs.

Parents are often delightfully surprised to find their baby listening intently to a song, or their two-year-old toddler singing out a familiar phrase. Very young children can be encouraged to sing "high-chair" graces, and also short responses such as "Thank you, God." Don't be dismayed if the tune is sung a little off key, or if a note or a word is missing. Beginners at singing need the same patient encouragement we give beginners at speaking.

Older children, too, love to sing in a family group. The singing can be in a group gathered around the piano, or it can be spontaneous. Families often sing as they do things together—clean the house or the yard, set the table, or pack a picnic lunch.

Special notes about home use follow some of the selections, but all of the songs in this book can be used for family singing.

SINGING IN CHURCH...

EVERY child of the Church should know the wonderful joy of congregational singing. Singing in the midst of people serving God is one of the best ways for youngsters to participate in the liturgical worship of the Church; it also helps them to feel a part of their parish family.

As children learn great Bible canticles and traditional service music, they are exposed, in a lively and practical way, to their Christian heritage. Lists of such church music from *The Hymnal 1940* will be found at the back of this song book. Hymns, too, are fre-

quently suggested. We hope clergymen and teachers exploring this book will find that several of its songs are also useful for family services.

Enjoying the music of the Church with children—at home, in a class, on a trip, or anywhere else—helps them to make it their own.

SINGING IN THE CLASSROOM...

SINGING with young children in church school or in any other group should be just as informal and as much fun as singing at home. To limit singing to a "special place" or a "special time" keeps children from expressing spontaneously in a song their feelings of wonder, sympathy, or delight. So sing with the children wherever they are.

Many of the songs in this book can be used to start a conversation or to conclude a story or short talk. "My Place in God's World" (#86) grew out of such a talk with second-graders. A song like "I Had a Feeling" (#138) may spark a discussion. Sometimes let the children sing as they work. "We're Making Valentines" (#151) is a good work song.

There are plenty of formal ways to use songs in a class or with a group of children. Primary children who have attended church with their families may want to start their class session with a sung prayer, or to end with a song before they go home. Younger boys and girls—in nursery and kindergarten—can learn a song for their offering, a song to sing on birthdays, or a grace to sing at juice time.

TEACHING NEW SONGS...

SING a new song in a way that tells the children you *like* it! Sing a song as you would tell a story, looking at the children so that they can see your face. Sing it with any actions the song may suggest. Be familiar with a song before you try to teach it, so that you won't have to watch the music all the time, or be held a captive at the piano.

Because a song *is* a song, and not a verse read aloud, keep the words and melody inseparable. Maybe it will be necessary to "line out" a song phrase by phrase while the children are learning it. But *sing* the phrase each time it is repeated. Asking the children to speak the words and then fit them to the melody is asking for extra work.

Learning a new song takes time, especially with very young children. Save enough time to sing new songs over and over, as well as to enjoy old favorites. One good way to introduce a new song is to play or sing the music while the children are doing something else—resting or playing or working at their tables.

When time for learning a new song is limited, use a few imaginative ways to vary the necessary repetition. One kindergarten teacher, rehearsing a Christmas song, delighted her class by suggesting in quick succession (1) pretending to carol outside the rector's home, (2) sending two children out of the room to the "stable" to "listen to the shepherds' song," (3) standing around the manger to sing for Mary and Joseph.

Many of the songs in this book have short refrains or phrases that children learn quickly. Let them sing "their part" while you sing "your part." Add other phrases to their part as you go along, and soon they will know the whole song. With more elaborate songs, we have suggested ways of breaking down the melody into shorter teaching units. Both "Funny" (#94) and "Here's the Proud Policeman" (#144) have such teaching aids printed below the music. Use these hints for other songs, too, if they are helpful.

We have sometimes set the same melody to different texts, which means that children need to learn only the words to some "new" songs. For example, for three closely related seasons of the Christian Year —Advent, Christmas, and Epiphany—the simple plainsong melody "Conditor alme" is used with "The Annunciation" (#1), "The Trip to Bethlehem" (#4), and "The Wise Men" (#15). A similar sequence is used for Palm Sunday, Easter, and Whitsunday—a traditional Cornish melody set to the texts of "To Jesus Christ the Children Sang" (#30), "It Is the Joyful Eastertime" (#34), and "It Is the Holy Spirit's Day" (#48).

Singing without a piano demands accuracy in "pitching" the song. If you are apt to begin a song too high or too low—and the latter is much more common—use a pitch pipe to sound the key note (almost always the last note of the melody). Flat, round chromatic pitch pipes, which sound every note between "F" and its higher octave, can be purchased through your local music store.

Teachers who have difficulty singing in tune often invite another adult—perhaps a member of the parish choir—to help with music. Such a person need not be a professional singer; an untrained voice which is fairly light and pleasing in quality may be just right for singing with children.

Many teachers find it helpful to make up a music "timetable" for several weeks in advance. They make a list of songs to fit their class plans and learn the songs they plan to use. For example, they make a list before Thanksgiving or Christmas or before they talk about homes, or prayer, or community helpers. Teachers can be prepared to meet nearly all occasions with a song if they build up a store of songs to draw on. A rainy Sunday, for instance, is bound to come along sooner or later. If you already know "On a Rainy Day" (#96) you can meet your class with a new game song. If the youngsters start talking about pets and animals, as they surely will, you can use the opportunity to sing "My Kitty" (#89) or "For Little Things" (#72).

TAILORING THE SONGS FOR DIFFERENT OCCASIONS...

UNDER many songs we have suggested ways to adapt the words to particular situations. The short litany at #75, for example, can easily include several other verses which children think up themselves. Encourage youngsters, especially at home, to sing new words to old songs. A fresh stanza helps a child make better use of his song. Even three-year-olds come up with astonishing (and useful) versions of familiar texts. Make other songs fit your class activities by similarly improvising words. Let our suggestions become springboards for new ideas, new actions, and perhaps even new songs.

SINGING ROUNDS...

OCCASIONALLY try singing as rounds those songs especially marked for them. One singer or group of singers begins the song, with the next group beginning at (1) when the first has arrived at (2). A third group may begin at (1) when the first group has arrived at (3). Singing the song through two or three times keeps it "going around" and is more fun. Many second- and third-graders have learned to sing rounds and do them very well.

ABOUT RHYTHMIC ACTIVITY...

MANY of these songs bring to mind actions to fit their rhythms. Be imaginative with your suggestions for acting out songs or moving to their music. Let the boys and girls explore their own ideas. We have provided music for such actions as walking, skipping, running, and marching. See "Rhythmic Activity" in the Topical Index at the back of the book for specific songs.

129

The Use of Music with Young Children

For rhythmic actions some teachers have also used music from *The Hymnal 1940*. Two illustrations are "All Hallows" (#96, 2nd tune) for marching and "Venite adoremus" (#41) for skipping. Use only the music.

MUSICAL SIGNALS...

To ANNOUNCE new activities, you can use music instead of speech. It is surprising how musical signals will cut into babbling voices and command attention. Signals can be as simple as:

(Quiet, please)

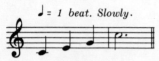

(Juice time)

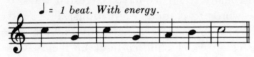

Or they may be more interesting:

(Time for a story. Come sit in a circle.)

(Sit down, please)

Be consistent. Always use the same signal to indicate the same activity.

Songs or song phrases also lend themselves to this purpose: "Put Away Song" (#153) is particularly useful; "Dolly's Lullaby" (#154), played softly, could be the signal for rest time; the refrain "O come, let us adore him" (*The Hymnal 1940*, #12), the refrain of "Dix" (*The Hymnal 1940*, #52), or some other familiar hymn could announce the time to gather for worship.

DECIDING THE SPEED FOR SINGING...

How fast should these songs be sung? In general, choose a tempo at which each musical phrase can be sung with one breath. Remember that children take shorter breaths than adults.

You may wonder why, with one exception (#11), no time signatures appear in the music. Many of the melodies have measures that change in length. Instead of interrupting a song with varying signatures, which might cause confusion, we have placed above the song the kind of note which is the basic pulse of the piece. This note should get one beat throughout the song, no matter how many beats are included in any one measure. Tunes we have taken from early American hymnals gain considerable excitement from their elastic measures. See the third measure of "It Makes No Difference, East or West" (#112), for example, with its sudden shift from three beats to two. Yet the beat itself continues at a constant speed.

Notation is, of course, visual, not aural. The youngsters will be aware only of the resulting rhythms. What seems difficult to teachers and parents often seems delightfully fresh to children. Boys and girls making up their own songs show little concern for our traditional concept of four-measure phrases with four beats in each measure.

Beside the beat-note above the songs we have also indicated the speed or manner in which the beats should be sung. That direction, along with the general principle of one breath per musical phrase, allows the freedom of choice necessary in different singing situations. The age of the children, the size of the group, the familiarity with the song, the size of the room, and the ability of the accompanist are other factors to consider in determining speed.

ACCOMPANYING THE SONGS...

Some songs need nothing but the singers. Others have two- and three-part accompaniments for either piano or organ. The four-part vocal harmonies taken from *The Hymnal 1940* are unchanged but have been written out as pianists would play them. Remember to play lightly; children's voices are light and clear. Thick organ registrations or harsh piano playing force the youngsters to sing too loudly and unpleasantly.

Playing the melody with its higher octave often supplies an adequate accompaniment. When there is a more descriptive accompaniment, first let the children learn the song, and then add the piano part as a special treat.

Some songs have chord-markings for the Autoharp. This is a useful, lightweight, zitherlike instru-

130

ment played by pressing down bars marked for different chords, and strumming on the strings. One or two strums per measure usually suffice. Autoharps, simple enough for the children themselves to play, are manufactured in two sizes: 5-chords and 12-chords. While we have used the larger size in our chord markings, many of them can be played on the smaller instrument. Autoharps are available through local music stores and currently sell in the price range of about $20 to $30.

Do not be limited to Autoharp, piano, or organ. A violin, flute, recorder, or clarinet accompaniment can add to the excitement of singing. For some songs a guitar makes a delightful accompaniment. Invite a boy or girl from the upper grades who plays one of these instruments to play for the youngsters while they sing. Young children can sing to the "music" they themselves make with rhythm instruments— drums, sticks, rattles, triangles, and so forth. Help them to choose the kind of instrument best suited to the tempo and mood of a particular song. Many classes of boys and girls make their own rhythm instruments. Books describing how are available in most libraries.

ABOUT THE PLAINSONG MELODIES . . .

Because young children have such a good time singing unusual songs, we have included several plainsong melodies. Boys and girls, far less trained than we in what is "familiar," generally find plainsong delightfully easy, for it involves no special rhythms to remember.

Part of the plainness of plainsong is the lack of any regular accents and rhythmic patterns. The notes are fairly even and they take their stresses from the words. Bar lines are breath marks, not measure indications. The smallest one (touching the two top lines of the staff) suggests a very quick breath, and the next larger (touching the three middle lines) suggests a more leisurely breath that does not, however, interrupt the flow of the melody.

Sing the melodies smoothly and easily. They are attractive tunes and most young children will learn them readily. If it becomes necessary to play an accompaniment, be certain that it is played lightly and flexibly.

AND FINALLY . . .

The most effective way to use music with children at home or at church is to enjoy it with them. Music gives a youngster an important (and happy) way to respond to God every day as he works or plays or prays. We hope that this book will help you "make a joyful noise unto the Lord" with your children.

Norman and Margaret Mealy

Some Hymns for Young Children from *The Hymnal 1940*

We have selected these hymns with two principles in mind. (1) The ideas expressed should be understandable to young children and true to their experience. (A few difficult words are more readily explained than difficult ideas.) (2) Direct language speaks to children better than extensive symbolism.

A number of "great hymns," favorites in particular parishes, might be added. While young children may not readily understand the words of such hymns, they will want to share in singing them with their parents. Some of these hymns are an important part of our Christian heritage.

Each hymn has been given an age-level designation: N = Nursery (three- and four-year-olds), K = Kindergarten (five-year-olds), and P = Primary (first through third grades). Many hymns listed under one topic can be used just as well at other times. Lenten hymns, for example, are useful throughout the year.

Some Hymns for Young Children

Season or Subject	Grade Level	First Line	Number: Stanza
Advent	P	Come, thou long-expected Jesus	1:1
	P	Creator of the stars of night	6:1 (1st tune)
	P	On Jordan's bank the Baptist's cry	10:1
	P	Our King and Saviour draweth nigh	Invitatory Antiphon to *Venite*
Christmas	P	A babe lies in the cradle	39:1, 4
	K P	Alleluia. Unto us a child is born	Invitatory Antiphon to *Venite*
	N K P	Away in a manger	43:1
	P	From heaven high I come to you (especially for pageants)	22:1, 2, 4
	P	Good Christian men, rejoice	31:1
	N	O come, all ye faithful	12:refrain only
	K		12:1
	P		12:1, 3
	P	O little town of Bethlehem	21:1
	P	Once in royal David's city	236:1, 2
	K	Silent night, holy night	33:1
	P		33:1, 2
	N	Sing, O sing, this blessèd morn	26:refrain only
	K P		26:1
		(The tune "Dix," at #52, can also be used.)	
	N K	The snow lay on the ground	41:1
	P		41:1, 2, 3
	P	What can I give him	44:4
	P	What child is this	36:1
	P	While shepherds watched their flocks (for listening or for pageants)	13
Epiphany	P	As with gladness men of old	52:1
	N K P	Come and worship	28:refrain only
	P	God my Father, loving me	239
	P	In Christ there is no East or West	263:1 (1st tune)
	P	In every clime, by every tongue	111:2
	P	On Jordan's bank the Baptist's cry	10:1
	P	Saw you never, in the twilight	50:1, 2 (1st tune)
	P	The first Nowell the angel did say	30:especially 3, 5
	P	We three kings of Orient are	51:1
	P	What can I give him	44:4
Lent	P	Day by day	429 (2nd tune)
	P	Father, we thank thee for the night (The tune "Mendon," at #218, can also be used.)	240:especially 2
	K	God my Father, loving me	239:1
	P		239:1–4
	N	Jesus, Son of God most high	232:3
	K P		232:1, 3–5
	K P	O come to my heart, Lord Jesus	321:refrain only
	P	Saviour, teach me, day by day	428:1
	P	Teach me, my God and King (The tune "Yattendon 46," at #481, can also be used.)	476:1
	P	The glory of these forty days	61:1
	P	There is a green hill far away	65:1
Palm Sunday	P	All glory, laud, and honor	62:refrain, 4, 6

Season or Subject	Grade Level	First Line	Number: Stanza
	K P	Jesus, Son of God most high	232:1
	P	There is a green hill far away	65:1
	P	When Jesus into Sion rode	331:3
Easter	K P	Alleluia. The Lord is risen indeed	Invitatory Antiphon to *Venite*
	P	Christ the Lord is risen to-day	95:1 (2nd tune)
	P	Jesus Christ is risen to-day	85:1, 4
	P	That Easter Day with joy was bright	98:1
Rogation	N K	We plow the fields, and scatter	138:refrain only
	P		138:1
Ascension	P	All glory, laud, and honor	62:refrain, 4, 6
	K P	Alleluia. Christ the Lord ascendeth into heaven	Invitatory Antiphon to *Venite*
	P	God my Father, loving me	239
	K	Hail the day that sees him rise	104:1st line (2nd tune)
	P	Lord Jesus, from thy throne above	250
Whitsunday	K P	Alleluia. The Spirit of the Lord filleth the world	Invitatory Antiphon to *Venite*
	P	Spirit divine, attend our prayers	370:1
Trinity	P	Father, Son, and Holy Ghost, one God	Invitatory Antiphon to *Venite*
	P	Father, Son, and Holy Spirit (Use "us" for "them.")	514:6
	P	Glory be to the Father	See end of *Venite*
	P	Holy, Holy, Holy!	266:1, 4
	K P	Praise God, from whom all blessings flow (Can also be sung, with alleluias, to the tune "Vigiles et Sancti," #599.)	139
God's Care and Love	P	All praise to thee, my God, this night	165:1, 4
	P	Father of mercy	238:1, 2
	N	God who made the earth	248:1
	K P		248:1, 2
	P	In Christ there is no East or West	263:1 (1st tune)
	K P	Lord, keep us safe this night (The tune "Venice," at #372, can also be used.)	174
	P	Now that the daylight fills the sky	159:1
God the Creator	K	All things bright and beautiful	311:1
	P		311:1–4
	P	*Benedicite,* choose an even number of verses (For music, see #57 in this book.)	
	K P	Can you count the stars	245:1
	N K	For the beauty of the earth	296:refrain only
	P		296:1, 2, 4
		(The tune "Dix," at #52, can also be used.)	
	N	God who made the earth	248:1
	K P		248:1, 2
	P	We thank you, Lord of Heaven	313:1
	P	We plow the fields, and scatter	138:1
Praise	P	All glory, laud, and honor	62:refrain, 4, 6
	P	Holy, Holy, Holy!	266:1, 4
	P	Let all the world in every corner sing	290:1 (1st tune)
	P	Lord Jesus, from thy throne above	250

133

Some Hymns for Young Children

Season or Subject	Grade Level	First Line	Number: Stanza
	K P	Praise God, from whom all blessings flow (Can also be sung, with alleluias, to the tune "Vigiles et Sancti," #599)	139
	K P	Through north and south and east and west	540
Thanksgiving	P	Come, ye thankful people, come	137:1
	N K	Now thank we all our God	276:1st line
	P		276:1
	N K	We plow the fields, and scatter	138:refrain only
	P		138:1
Thanks for Special Things	P	All praise to thee, my God, this night	165:1, 4
	K P	Father, we thank thee for the night (The tune "Mendon," at #218, can also be used.)	240:1
	P	For the beauty of the earth (The tune "Dix," at #52, can also be used.)	296:1, 2, 4
	P	We thank you, Lord of Heaven	313:1
Me	P	All praise to thee, my God, this night	165:1
	K	God my Father, loving me	239:1
	P		239:1-4
	N	God who made the earth	248:1
	K P		248:1, 2
	K	I sing a song of the saints of God	243:1
	P		243:1-3
	K	I worship thee, Lord Jesus	252:5
	P		252:1, 5
	P	Saviour, teach me, day by day	428:1
	P	Teach me, my God and King (The tune "Yattendon 46," at #481, can also be used.)	476:1
Family	P	For the joy of human love (The tune "Dix," at #52, can also be used.)	296:4
	P	Holy Father, in thy mercy	514:1, 6
Friends and Neighbors	N	Jesus, Son of God most high	232:3
	K P		232:1, 2, 3
	K	I sing a song of the saints of God	243:1
	P		243:1-3
Saints	P	For thy dear saints, O Lord	124:1
	K	I sing a song of the saints of God	243:1
	P		243:1-3
	P	The Lord is glorious, in his saints	Invitatory Antiphon to *Venite*
Morning	K	Father, we thank thee for the night	240:1
	P		240:1, 2
		(The tune "Mendon," at #218, can also be used.)	
	P	Now that the daylight fills the sky	159:1
Evening	P	All praise to thee, my God, this night	165:1, 4
	K P	Lord, keep us safe this night (The tune "Venice," at #372, can also be used.)	174
	P	Now the day is over	172:1, 2 (1st tune)
134 *Baptism*	P	O Jesus Christ, our Lord most dear	185:1

Season or Subject	Grade Level	First Line	Number: Stanza
Holy Communion	P	Jesus, gentlest Saviour	348 : 1
	P	Lord Jesus, from thy throne above	250
	P	Thy Gospel, Jesus, we believe	249
Missions	P	Father of mercy	238 : 1, 2
	P	In Christ there is no East or West	263 : 1 (1st tune)
	P	In every clime, by every tongue	111 : 2
	P	Remember all the people	262
	K P	Through north and south and east and west	540
Offering	N K P	All good gifts around us	138 : refrain
	K P	Praise God, from whom all blessings flow	139
	P	We give thee but thine own	481
Litany	N	Jesus, Son of God most high	232 : 3
	K P		232 : 1–5

Suggested Service Music from *The Hymnal 1940*

PARISH TRADITIONS will determine which of the following would be useful. All chant and page numbers refer to the full music edition.

MORNING PRAYER

K P *Preces* (O Lord, open thou our lips . . .): #601, *pp*.699–700

K P *Invitatory Antiphons: p.* 704

K P *Venite:* Use the first verse for Kindergarten. For Primary begin by teaching one or two verses and the "Gloria Patri" (which the children need to learn early, for it is used so frequently). Gradually include other verses. Sing one of the melodies familiar to the parish (so that the children may more easily sing chants at home and in church or church school services). Be sure to follow the directions for "speech-rhythm" chanting on *p.* 697.

P *Benedicite:* Use other verses to add to those already in this book.

K P *Jubilate Deo:* See suggestions for the "Venite."

K P *Salutation* (The Lord be with you . . .): #601, *p.* 701

P *The Lord's Prayer:* Sing in monotone with the "Amen" as noted at #601, *p.* 701.

P *Versicles and responses:* #601, *pp.* 701–703

N K P *Amens:* Children quickly respond to prayers which are sung. Use the traditional musical inflections for prayers found in *The Choral Service* (published under the direction of General Convention by H. W. Gray Co., N.Y.).

K P *Psalms:* Particular verses from psalms in the back of the Hymnal may be sung to chant melodies already familiar to the children.

HOLY COMMUNION

HAVE the children sing these (each stands by itself) as songs for different occasions.

K P *Kyrie eleison:* #702, #709

P *Sanctus:* #704, #711 (more difficult)

N K P *Gloria tibi:* #730 (Sing as you would speak it, and preferably without accompaniment.)

P *Sursum corda:* #734

K P *Gloria in excelsis:* #738, #739 (Sing either melody as you would speak the words.) First two sentences only.

135

A Selected List of Hymnals and Songbooks
for Additional Materials

God's Wonderful World. Agnes Leckie Mason and Phyllis Brown Ohanian. Random House (cloth) or New American Library of World Literature (paper), N.Y., 1954. (Nursery, Kindergarten, and a few Primary)

Hymns and Songs for the Church Kindergarten. Margaret Cropper and A. R. B. Wylam, editors. The National Society, London, n.d. (Kindergarten and Primary)

Kindergarten Songs and Rhythms. Compiled by Margaret L. Crain. The Judson Press, Philadelphia, 1954. Record album and book.

Nursery Songs and Rhythms. Compiled by Margaret L. Crain. The Judson Press, Philadelphia, 1953. Record album and book.

Songs for Early Childhood at Church and Home. The Westminster Press, Philadelphia, 1958. (Nursery and Kindergarten)

The Whole World Singing. Compiled by Edith Lovell Thomas. Friendship Press, N.Y., 1950. (Primary and Junior. Many songs from other countries.)

American Folk Songs for Children. Ruth Crawford Seeger. Doubleday & Company, N.Y., 1948. (Nursery, Kindergarten, Primary, with many suggestions for teachers.)

Music for Early Childhood. "New Music Horizons Series." Silver Burdett Company, N.Y., 1952. (Nursery, Kindergarten, Primary, with many suggestions for teachers.) Recordings available to use with this book.

Singing Time. Satis N. Coleman and Alice G. Thorn. The John Day Co., N. Y., 1929. (Nursery)

Songs for the Nursery School. Laura Pendleton MacCarteney. Willis Music Co., Cincinnati, 1937.

The Kindergarten Book. "Our Singing World Series." Lilla Belle Pitts, Mabelle Glenn, and Lorrain E. Watters, editors. Ginn & Company, Boston, 1949.

Creative Rhythmic Movement for Children. Gladys Andrews. Prentice-Hall, N.Y., 1954. (Includes practical suggestions for making musical instruments.)

There's Music in Children. Emma D. Sheehy. Holt, Rinehart & Winston, N.Y., 1952. (Contains many ideas about teaching music to young children.)

Topical Index of Songs

Index of Song Titles and First Lines

The letters N, K, and P indicate the age range at which each song will probably be most suitable. "N" stands for Nursery (three- and four-year-olds); "K" for Kindergarten (five-year-olds); and "P" for Primary (first through third grades). First lines are in italics.